DINOSAUR DIGS

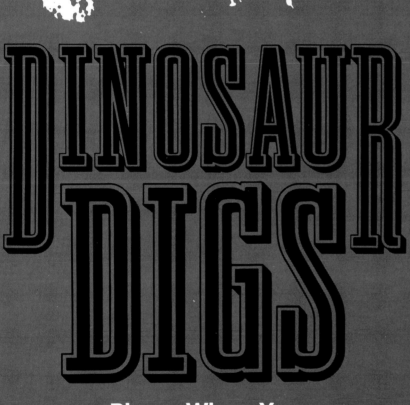

DINOSAUR DIGS

Places Where You Can Discover Prehistoric Creatures

by Richard Will, Ph.D.
and Margery Read

DINOSAUR DIGS:
Places Where You Can Discover Prehistoric Creatures

Published by Country Roads Press
P.O. Box 286, Lower Main Street
Castine, Maine 04421

Designed by Studio 3, Ellsworth, Maine.

Cover photo courtesy Cleveland Museum of Natural History, Cleveland, Ohio.

ISBN 1-56626-004-3

Library of Congress Catalog Card No. 92-073118

Printed in the United States of America

10 9 8 7 6 5 4 3 2 1

To our dino-maine-iacs:

Johana, Emily, Valerie, Daniel,
Aaron, Logan,
Anna-Maria, Benjamin,
Colby, Brandon,
Alex, Emily, and Katie

© VICTORIA SHERIDAN 1992

Boaters drift past Tiger Wall on the wild Yampa River. Dinosaur National Monument.

Contents

Introduction

Fascination with prehistoric animals has spanned several centuries, inspired generations of scholarship, bridged the generation gap between parents and children, and fueled a lucrative entertainment industry. Libraries are filled with books — both factual and fanciful — about animals that roamed the earth long ago. Museums stack fossil bone upon fossil bone in an impassioned effort to revitalize these marvelous and fantastic creatures. Movies and television create images and scenarios that are very often colorful and only sometimes accurate. And we resurrect prehistoric animals in popular material culture ranging from T-shirts and plastic models to stickers and even pencils erasers. That's pretty broad societal impact from assorted old bones!

These days, dinosaurs seem to be more popular than ever, and everywhere you look there are new books about them. But we think *Dinosaur Digs* is different. We didn't set out to simply tell another dinosaur story. Instead, our primary objective was to compile information on some of the most exciting places in the United States and Canada for seeing and learning about prehistoric creatures — and to make that information as accessible as we could.

Our research began with an extensive mailing campaign to museums, parks, and related organizations across the states and provinces. After many months and more than a few phone calls, we amassed a pile of slides, pictures, brochures, and other documents describing some of the best "dinosaur digs" on the continent — plus information for the adventurous spirits among you who are looking for the rare experience of volunteering on a dig. Using a format similar to a guidebook, we assembled this material so you can

quickly spot the places you'd like to visit on vacation or explore as a volunteer.

Along the way, we delve into some of the more intriguing and persistent questions that surround prehistoric animals: When and how long did they live? What did they eat? What color were they? How did they come to be preserved for scientists to study? And why in the world did they become extinct? Each year, discoveries in paleontology, archaeology, and geology add new pages to the story of prehistoric life, and new theories and hypotheses continually demand that those pages be revised. We make no claim to be exhaustive in our research, nor was that our objective. Rather, we cover the ways scientists have studied prehistoric animals and what they are thinking about dinosaurs today to prepare you for your visits to museums and parks. When we see the complexity of sorting out fact from fiction and keeping abreast of the latest paleontological thinking, we can appreciate the stupendous efforts made by park and museum staffs to reconstruct prehistoric creatures and their habitats for us to enjoy.

Dinosaur Digs was written for the general public, and especially for families with children who want to share the thrill of discovering these wondrous creatures together. And for those whose curiosity extends beyond these covers – and we suspect there will be many – we provide a selected bibliography ("Dinosources") for both children and adults.

We hope you enjoy your excursions among the dinosaurs.

— R.W. & M.R.

1
Meeting Dinosaurs

When you and your child stand and look up at a dinosaur skeleton in a museum, or explore the parks where they are quarried, you are sharing people's centuries-old fascination with dinosaurs. They lived so long ago; they seem so different from the animals we're familiar with; and some of them are just so BIG. . . .

Our imaginations shift into overdrive when we try to compare these behemoths with something in our modern environment: a tractor-trailer? an airplane? a football field? A hundred years ago, the *Brontosaurus* skeleton purchased by philanthropist Andrew Carnegie was tall enough – when it stood on its hind legs – to peer into the eleventh story of a remarkable new skyscraper, the New York Life Building. In the late 1700s, the French naturalist Georges Cuvier described megalosaur bones in terms of an elephant, the largest, most impressive animal he knew from the specimen in a Paris zoo. In every era since the first dinosaur discoveries, the human mind has boggled at these amazing creatures.

In the past 150 years or so since they were first recognized and described, we have learned a tremendous amount about dinosaurs. This is especially astounding when you realize that all this knowledge is based on fossils: no one has ever seen a dinosaur in the flesh – not even a dead one.

A Quick Look Back

Dinosaur bones have been turning up for centuries, but for a long time no one knew what they were. Quarry workers, peat cutters, and plowmen unearthed huge bones all over Europe. If we are awed by these great old bones today, imagine what people centuries ago must have thought about the bones – some as big as a man – they uncovered with the shovel or plow!

To explain these bones, people first thought of giants. In 1677 Robert Plot, a professor of chemistry at Oxford, described what were probably the condyles of

a megalosaur (great lizard) femur as a giant's scrotum. While people in the seventeenth century may have generally believed in giants, it's hard to believe anyone would accept seriously the idea of a twenty-pound scrotum, two feet around, which had turned to stone. Interestingly enough, halfway around the world and a hundred and fifty years earlier, the idea of giants had also occurred to the Aztecs; they presented Cortez with a huge fossilized bone (probably a mastodon femur) to prove that the Indians of Mexico descended from a race of giants.

As science became more sophisticated, so did the interpretation of dinosaurs. Probably the very first person to recognize fossilized reptile bones for what they were was Georges Cuvier, a brilliant late-eighteenth-century French anatomist and the first paleontologist. Cuvier was in the midst of identifying what appeared to be ancient elephant bones,* unearthed in Paris, of all places, when French troops fighting in the Netherlands shipped home the yard-long jaws of another monstrous animal. Cuvier examined the jaws, comparing them to

(Left) *T. rex*. Boston Museum of Science.

* Later identified as a mastodon bone.

(Above) Introducing *Triceratops*. Courtesy of the Royal Tyrrell Museum of Palaeontology, Alberta.

known animals, and determined they belonged to a great marine lizard, later christened mosasaur (sea lizard). Fossilized skeletons are rarely complete: from a few huge teeth and perhaps a femur and vertebra or two, early scientists speculated about entire forty-foot animals.

Reverend William Buckland of Oxford University and Dr. Gideon Mantell, a Victorian gentleman scientist, first described and named true dinosaurs: Buckland's "Notice on the Megalosaurus or Great Fossil Lizard of Stonesfield" appeared in 1824 and Mantell's treatise on the *Iguanodon* teeth and bones he and his wife discovered came out three years later. From then on dinosaur discoveries came thick and fast.

In an address to the British Association for the Advancement of Science in 1841, Dr. Richard Owen of

Great Exposition, were moved to a park and decorated with models of the giant lizards. Sculptor Benjamin Waterhouse Hawkins set about "revivifying the ancient world" under the watchful eye of Professor Owen. Hawkins spent the better part of 1854 fashioning brick, stone, cement, and iron into life-sized models of early aquatic reptiles such as megalosaurs, ichthyosaurs, and plesiosaurs, *Iguanodons,* ancient amphibians, crocodiles, and mammals. These were arranged in the glass house and among the trees of Sydenham outside London where they can still be seen today.

Like many scientists of the day, Mr. Hawkins depended a great deal on imagination for his reconstructions: his *Iguanodon* has a horn like a reptilian rhinoceros; others resemble large versions of modern frogs and turtles. But Victorians weren't too concerned

the British Museum coined the word *dinosaur* — meaning "terrible lizard" — to distinguish the fossil remains of extinct animals from those of modern reptiles. Owen created the concept of dinosaurs we have today: huge, extinct, reptilian creatures.

All of Victorian England was excited by the idea of dinosaurs. At the suggestion of Prince Albert, the glass vaults of the Crystal Palace, site of London's 1851

about plausibility; they just loved dinosaurs. In fact, they were so enamored with the giant reptiles that the city of Maidstone (where a nearly complete *Iguanodon* skeleton was found) voted to emblazon its civic coat of arms with an "Iguanodon Proper." From all over England, people flocked to the Crystal Palace to "witness the monsters that inhabited the earth before Noah."

(Right) Swift *Deinonychus*—"terrible claw"—dinosaurs stalk their prey at the California Academy of Sciences, San Francisco.

To celebrate the nearly completed construction, Hawkins and Owen held a dinner party for paleontology's elite *inside* a partially finished *Iguanodon,* a massive structure of 600 bricks, 1,500 tiles, and several tons of cement. Owen's place at the head of the table was naturally at the head of the *Iguanodon.* Ignoring the flat, plant-crushing teeth of the dinosaur, the magazine *Punch* remarked, "We congratulate the company on the era in which they live, for if it had been an early geological period they might perhaps have occupied the *Iguanodon*'s inside without having any dinner there."

On the other side of the Atlantic, what was probably America's first dinosaur bone discovery was unearthed in New Jersey and reported to a Philadelphia scientific society in 1787, but no one seems to have known what it was and unfortunately the bone has disappeared. However, in 1806 William Clark (of Lewis and Clark) wrote in his journal of finding huge rib bones, which he attributed to fish, in Montana rocks. More than likely, these were dinosaur bones.

In 1800 a farm boy discovered enormous three-toed footprints in the sandstone of Massachusetts. Edward Hitchcock of Amherst College became interested in these Connecticut River Valley footprints and published an article about them in 1848, attributing them to huge birds. No matter what Hitchcock wrote, locals continued to believe these were footprints of "Noah's raven," a bird extinct because it was too big for the Ark. It may seem incongruous to have confused birds and dinosaurs, but more and more modern dinosaur research indicates Hitchcock was on the right track, as dinosaurs and birds are ever more closely related by paleontologists.

From fragments of jaw, teeth, limbs, feet, pelvis, and twenty-eight vertebrae found in New Jersey in 1858, Dr. Joseph Leidy of Philadelphia constructed a bipedal hadrosaur (duckbilled dinosaur), the first assembled dinosaur skeleton ever displayed in a museum. Now people could go to a museum, see for themselves how big an animal a dinosaur was, and imagine it roaming through their farmyards back in New Jersey. It was immensely popular.

There was so much demand from the public for more dinosaur skeletons like the one in Philadelphia that major museums all over the East hired scientists and mounted fossil-finding expeditions. In the 1870s

The battle is joined: *Allosaurus* vs. *Camptosaurus*. Photo by Susan Middleton; courtesy California Academy of Sciences, San Francisco.

and '80s in North America the science of paleontology and the number of excavated dinosaurs grew by leaps and bounds as huge discoveries were made in Utah, Colorado, Wyoming, and Montana. In Wyoming, dinosaur bones lay so thick on the ground that a shepherd built himself a hut of dinosaur bones in a spot paleontologists later christened Bone Cabin Quarry. During the "bone rush" of the late 1800s, hundreds of tons of specimens were shipped to museums back East.

The early reconstruction of dinosaurs was pretty primitive. So much of it was guesswork; so few fossil skeletons were complete. Even the greats like Edward Drinker Cope made mistakes. When O.C. Marsh of Yale pointed out that the 50-foot *Elasmosaurus* (ribbon dinosaur) that Cope had assembled at the Philadelphia Museum had its vertebrae the wrong way round, he touched off the legendary feud between them. (More about the Cope–Marsh rivalry in Chapter 6, with the information on the Garden Park Fossil Area in Colorado.)

Catching Up with the Present

Many modern museums are still rearranging their dinosaur bones. In fact, it was not until 1979 that the *Apatosaurus* at the Carnegie Museum got the right head. Recently, museums have also improved dinosaur posture. Traditional museum dinosaurs were posed in a tails-down, splayed, out-at-the-elbows stance like a crocodile. Today, the huge sauropods (lizard-hipped dinosaurs) like *Apatosaurus* and *Diplodocus* no longer just drag their tails on the ground or remain on all fours. Today's dinosaurs stand up straight and tall.

Much of our thinking about dinosaurs has changed also. Their birthdays have moved back in time and their capabilities have moved forward on the evolutionary scale. Modern paleontologists believe some dinosaurs were clever, swift predators or social beings that moved in herds and cared for their young. Bright colors, warm-bloodedness (or at least some of the attributes of warm-bloodedness), and close links to birds are also presently fashionable for dinosaurs.

The story of *Archaeopteryx* is a good example of how thinking about dinosaurs has changed. In 1861 a Bavarian workman turned up a two-foot-long fossilized bird from the Jurassic Period (see Chapter 3) which eventually wound up at the British Museum and set the world of evolutionists and paleontologists in a tailspin. Christened *Archaeopteryx,* or "ancient wing," it had long flight feathers on arms and wrists and big tail feathers dangling behind from a bony tail. The prints of the feathers were clear on the limestone. Despite these birdlike characteristics, it had teeth instead of a beak, scales instead of body feathers, and perching claws like a dinosaur.

For such a small animal, it has stirred a lot of debate. Thomas Huxley, who championed Charles Darwin's theories in *The Origin of Species* (1859), seized on *Archaeopteryx* as the missing link Darwin had hypothesized to bridge the evolutionary gap between reptiles and modern birds. Papers were presented at learned societies; controversy flared.

Archaeopteryx was the size of a crow. It lived as an early shore bird, climbing and leaping among the low shore and island shrubs, probably nesting among the bushes and patrolling the shoreline and lagoons for fish and squid. It flew by flapping and gliding. The move from land to air is as momentous as the move from water to land 400 million years ago. Today we accept *Archaeopteryx* as a pioneer aviator, but controversy over classifying it as a bird or a dinosaur still rages. Adding to the confusion are the skeletal remains, recently turned up in Texas, of what may be an even earlier bird ancestor.

Many such new discoveries blur our traditional concepts of dinosaurs, but today's definition includes the following:

1 Dinosaurs are reptiles that lived in the Mesozoic Era 248 to 65 million years ago. They rose in the Triassic Period, flourished in the Jurassic Period, and vanished by the end of the Cretaceous Period (see Chapter 3). They were the dominant land animal for about 135 million years and gave rise to a new animal, the bird, which continues to be successful. They had scaly skin and (sometimes) ponderous tails, and laid eggs. Some of them were indeed "terrible lizards" four stories tall, but some were not-so-terrible creatures the size of a chicken.

2 Dinosaurs walked erect; no out-at-the-elbows, crocodile posture for them. Only *Triceratops* and its relatives had sprawled front legs, an adaptation that probably added stability in horned combat. (If a Mesozoic

Early drawing of *Archaeopteryx*.

animal had wings or flippers, like pterosaurs or icthyosaurs, it was not a true dinosaur.) This erect posture — a new type of body support and posture in the evolutionary scale — allowed dinosaurs to move efficiently on land and contributed to their success. So far scientists have identified about 500 different species of dinosaurs — about a quarter of these in the past dozen years — and new species are being added all the time.

3 Dinosaurs lived primarily on land. Some dinosaurs like *Diplodocus* and *Apatosaurus* spent a lot of time

Plant-eating dinosaurs had cheeks and specialized teeth that allowed them to chew food like leaves and grasses. Most modern reptiles have no cheeks; they eat mostly meat which they must swallow whole. Since we know almost nothing about dinosaurs in the flesh, we can't add to this definition many of the characteristics, such as number of heart chambers and complexity of blood cells, that set apart the other families and orders of animals.

5 Dinosaurs are divided into two groups: **Saurischians**

in the water and could swim, but no dinosaurs lived underwater or in the air. Pterosaurs (flyers) and icthyosaurs, plesiosaurs, and mosasaurs (swimmers) have skeletal differences from true dinosaurs. Where to put *Archaeopteryx* in this definition still remains a problem.

4 Dinosaurs had special skeletal adaptations that distinguished them from other reptiles. They had three to ten fused sacral vertebrae to support their weight at the hips; reptiles have only two. Their skulls were lightened with "windows." They had special hip sockets to accommodate their great weight and straight femurs.

(sometimes called sauropods) or lizard-hipped dinosaurs like *Tyrannosaurus rex,* and **Ornithischians,** or bird-hipped dinosaurs like *Stegosaurus.*

Traditionally, paleontology has dealt only with finding and classifying dinosaurs, but modern scientists are more interested in the intriguing questions raised by all these discoveries. How did dinosaurs live? Were they warm-blooded? Did they raise their young? Travel in herds and migrate? The unanswered questions, ever-changing theories, and unexpected discoveries keep both scientists and dinosaur fans on their toes and perpetually fascinated.

(Above) *Stegosaurus.* Courtesy Denver Museum of Natural History, Denver, Colorado.

(Right) A mother *Barosaurus* defends her young from a hungry *Allosaurus* on the prowl. Mural by John Gurche; courtesy American Museum of Natural History, New York.

2
Terrible Lizards
& Mega-Mammals

The late-afternoon sun warmed the old Triceratops *as she lumbered around the lake margin. Every ponderous footstep left an impression in the soft mud. Her ancient eyes searched warily for signs of predators, but her nostrils were filled with the fresh smell of tender spring vegetation that beckoned, waiting to be eaten. A shadow momentarily obscured the warming rays of sunlight on her shoulders when a leather-winged creature glided twenty feet above her head. It flew west toward a volcanic outcrop with a small, limp animal dangling in its sharp-toothed jaws.*

The forest was unusually quiet for this time of day, and very few animals were feeding by the lakeshore. A single swan-like neck that terminated in a tiny head swayed several hundred feet offshore. The only evidence of the creature's actual size was an island of partially submerged back that followed a couple of dozen feet behind the swaying neck. The swimming animal caused a perceptible ripple in the otherwise unbroken surface of the lake and tiny waves splashed on shore.

The tired Triceratops *stopped for a moment to feed on the fronds of young ferns. Her wrinkled back bore the scars of many battles, but her beautiful colors were as vivid as the day she had hatched from an egg more than fifty years before. Orange and yellow eye rings and red stripes that streaked down her sides and around her legs distinguished her species. Three horns, one just above her nose and two others just behind and above her yellow eyes, protruded from her massive face to make her a formidable adversary. The left horn had been severely chipped in a battle for nesting space in the valley where she had returned many times to lay her clutch of eggs. The tip of the right horn had been lost in a fierce fight that had nearly cost her her life — a struggle with a young but dangerous* Tyrannosaurus rex. *She wore a collar-like mantle of scarred, skin-covered bone that gave her an almost regal appearance and at the same time afforded some protection to the soft neck flesh that lay behind it.*

No more than fifty feet away from where she was feeding stood a wall of sandstone, trees, and brush. Behind the rocks a Tyrannosaurus *crouched motionless except for the regular swelling of its sides as it breathed. The rex's nostrils caught the rich scent of the nearby* Triceratops. *The huge carnivore had not gorged for several days, and the gnawing hunger in his stomach had forced him to concentrate all of his attention on obtaining a meal. His massive hind limbs trembled in anticipation. Without even looking out from behind his cover, the hungry dinosaur knew that the* Triceratops *was very nearby, and he waited patiently to see if she would draw closer.*

The browsing Triceratops *followed the path of lush vegetation leading up to the sandstone wall. She was so close that the tyrannosaur could hear her stomach rumbling as it digested the leaves and twigs.*

Suddenly, with lightning speed, the tyrannosaur sprang from behind the rock wall into the path of the Triceratops. *His cavernous jaws opened wide to expose a deadly set of six-inch razor-sharp teeth.*

The old female froze in surprise. She had sensed no danger. Realizing escape was impossible, she lowered her massive head, bellowed, and charged the huge rex. Side-stepping her charge, the tyrannosaur danced out of reach of the Triceratops's *lethal horns.*

Before the old dinosaur could wheel about to charge again, the agile tyrannosaur jumped onto her back, firmly clamped his powerful jaws, and tore a great, gaping hole in the soft flesh of her neck. Vertabrae snapped; blood streamed to the ground. Dazed and mortally wounded, she panted in pain for no more than a couple of minutes until her life drained away.

This is the picture we all have of dinosaurs — those "terrible lizards": monumental beasts engaged in epic battles that took place on the shores of shallow lakes millions of years ago. But dinosaurs started small.

The broad outline of dinosaur evolution unfolds with small dinosaurs appearing about 225 million years ago. (See Chapter 3 for a discussion of geologic time periods.) The world was a very different kind of place then, when all of our modern continents were a single land mass we call Pangaea. Earth was warmer and drier, and only some of the plants that grew then would look familiar today: huge tree-ferns swayed in gentle breezes; conifers, palmlike cycads, ginkgos, and horsetails provided shade and food for many of the animals of that time. Reptile innovations such as self-contained, moisture-retaining eggs, protective water-proof skins, and speedy, agile two-legged locomotion gradually separated dinosaurs from the slow, watery world of the amphibian and opened a whole new way of life to them.

While the evolution of dinosaurs continued at a steady pace, other animals and plants also continued to evolve, and birds, mammals, and flowering plants first made their appearance. Dinosaurs diversified, became both plant and meat eaters, ranged in size from a chicken to a four-story building, and inhabited what are now all the modern continents. Because they inhabited so many different niches in the ecosystem over a period spanning 135 million years, dinosaurs developed many adaptations to suit various climates and topographies.

When vegetation stretched across the continents —

T. rex dines on *Triceratops*. Courtesy Milwaukee Public Museum.

green, toothsome, and inviting—some enterprising dinosaurs gave up meat and began to dine on something different. These early herbivores had almost unlimited food available if only they could chew and digest it: the salad bar required some dental and jaw modifications. If you've ever watched a snake wrestle to swallow a frog whole, you'll understand why chewing was a great evolutionary step forward. Dinosaur evolution and plant evolution took place simultaneously as ferns, cycads, and conifers gave rise to flowering plants with seeds.

A family portrait. Courtesy of Boston Museum of Science.

Food for Thought

Have you ever wondered how an enormous animal like *Apatosaurus* or *Diplodocus* could feed itself with such a tiny head? Look at the teeth: they don't amount to much. Modern plant-eating animals have a much more impressive array with grinding molars to process plant material. American paleontologist Robert Bakker points out that the two-foot head at the end of the 70-foot *Diplodocus* neck would have allowed it to browse among the treetops and eat pine needles. We know that *Diplodocus*'s teeth wore out and were continuously replaced in a way consistent with such a fibrous diet, but he did not have grinding molars to pulverize all that tough stuff. So how *did* he do it?

This mystery puzzled paleontologists for a long time. Initially, they ignored the problem by giving these plant-eating dinosaurs the metabolism (and the brain power) of something slightly more advanced than a cactus. But modern theories on the metabolism and intelligence of dinosaurs have reintroduced the quandary of how apatosaurs—who are estimated to have consumed about 1¾ tons of food a *day*—managed to chew it and digest it.

The answer seems to lie in the smooth, polished stones scientists have found in and around the skeletons of dinosaurs. These are gastroliths, or dinosaur gizzard stones, and they are often types of stones not found locally. Like birds and modern crocodiles, these sauropods may have gone out of their way to find and swallow carefully selected, rounded stones to pulverize their tough, fibrous food in a squeezing, grinding, muscular stomach or gizzard.

Variety in Shape and Size... And Some You'd Even Recognize

Probably you have noticed there are dinosaurs from 180 million years ago that look a lot like modern animals. *Triceratops* looks like a rhinoceros—large, strong, and horned—and he lived like a rhinoceros. He ate low, scrubby vegetation and relied on his horns, tough hide, and strong muscles to protect him. Even a tyrannosaur was careful about tackling a healthy adult *Triceratops* just as modern hunters are wary of the rhi-

no. Scarred bony frills found on *Triceratops* fossils suggest he was as short-tempered and pugnacious as a modern rhino, too.

Equivalent habitats and niches were occupied by similar animals. Completely unrelated animals that occupied the same niche in different times or places evolved parallel types of locomotion, feeding, defense, and attack — as dictated by the niche. *Struthiomimus*, which means "like an ostrich," lived on open sandy plains like his namesake. Tall, long-legged, and long-necked, both reptile and bird rely on a wary, observant eye and a pair of swift feet to protect them from predators. Since food is scarce in desert areas, their diet was (or is) omnivorous. Ostriches added feathers and replaced teeth with a beak, but the two animals are quite similar despite the millions of years separating them.

The bristle-toothed Argentine *Pterodactyl* pursued a flamingolike life-style. Possessing long legs for wading and a long neck for reaching, he dined on shrimp and algae which were strained through his specially adapted beak. The flamingo's strainer apparatus is in his upper jaw — which explains the headstands he performs at dinner — while the *Pterodactyl*'s bristle-toothed strainer was in his lower jaw for more graceful dining.

Like armadillos, tank-like ankylosaurs were covered with bony plates. Low to the ground, they flattened themselves even further and relied on their armor and tails for defense just as armadillos do today. Armadillos have spread across the United States from arid Mexico to the Florida Everglades. Ankylosaurs have also been found in both desert and swampy areas where, like their modern look-alikes, they probably ate soft foods found close to the ground.

Pieces of the Past

How do we reconstruct the appearance, life-style, and life-and-death struggles of creatures that lived over a hundred million years ago — just from a collection of old bones? To answer this question it is important to separate what the fossils can actually tell us from what we add with the aid of analogy, educated guesswork, and artistic license.

Fossilized bones have important stories to tell about the size and shape of the animals whose flesh once covered them. Places where muscles once attached show scarring on the bone surface that hints at how powerful these animals may have been. Tiny holes preserved in the bone walls show the supply of blood that once nourished the creatures' bodies. Teeth and jaw structures provide evidence of diet, and cranial capacity indicates possible intelligence. Taken together, these various lines of evidence allow paleontologists to clothe their fossil finds in muscle and skin

with reasonable accuracy. Just as an anatomist can estimate the appearance and certain physical characteristics of a person from his or her skeleton, so can a paleontologist perform a similar miracle with his collection of fossilized dinosaur remains.

(Top) Skull of a *Triceratops*, a common Montana resident 70 million years ago. Photo by Marshall Lambert; courtesy Carter County Museum, Ekalaka, Montana.

(Above) Handle with care: a paleontologist gently uncovers a clutch of dinosaur eggs discovered in Mongolia. Photo courtesy American Museum of Natural History, New York.

Sometimes fossils can confirm (or refute) our ideas about dinosaurs. For example, paleontologists had always assumed that dinosaurs—like reptiles today—laid eggs. But until the dashing Roy Chapman Andrews of the American Museum of Natural History turned up fossil specimens in Mongolia in the 1920s, dinosaur eggs were only an educated guess. In our overall understanding of dinosaurs, eggs with hard shells—which could be laid far away from water—placed the animals firmly on dry land. The reptile egg was a complete life-support system, as independent of changes in the weather as a space capsule. Dinosaurs also developed tough, dry hides that conserved their body moisture, another innovation that took them out of the puddles and swamps and into the forests and plains. But until paleontologists turned up molds of dinosaur skin and even a rare bit of fossilized dinosaur skin (which you can see at the American Museum of Natural History), no one was sure what kind of skin they had.

However, just as the anatomist cannot tell from a collection of human bones how the person dressed, whether he or she wore jewelry or liked to attend the opera, a paleontologist cannot be confident about the color of a dinosaur's skin or eyes or about the behaviors that characterized it. Information for this part of our reconstruction must come from other sources.

The carefully recorded context of fossil remains can tell us something about the *environment* in which dinosaurs lived. Catastrophic events such as flash floods and mud slides that resulted in rapid burial of large areas, have preserved glimpses of dinosaur *families.* Nests and eggs like those found in China (and later in Montana) hint much about dinosaur reproductive behavior and group living just as bird rookeries show us certain characteristics about the behavior of the birds that inhabit them. Careful study of evolutionary relationships has provided clues to dinosaur *similarities with other creatures* that preceded and followed them. And the cautious use of analogy to modern animals has helped explain *how dinosaurs interacted with one another* on the prehistoric landscape. Educated guesses based on these glimpses, hints, clues, and analogies help "fill in some of the blanks" concerning dinosaur life.

Artistic license plays its greatest role in coloring not only the prehistoric landscape but also the creatures that dominated it. What color were dinosaurs? This simple question is the one most frequently asked of paleontologists—and the one they have the least amount of data to answer. Modern reptiles can be brightly colored (think of Gila monsters and coral snakes) and certainly their modern relatives the birds are snappy dressers. Unfortunately, although we have a few fossil records of skin, it is impossible to know what color it was. It *is* possible, however, to make an educated guess based on our current knowledge of color in nature.

Color serves as camouflage, as a sexual attractant, as a warning, and as a way of mimicking other animals, and dinosaurs almost certainly had good color vision.

It is quite possible that some small dinosaurs were poisonous to eat and distinctively colored (like certain amphibians and butterflies today) to warn off potential diners. Other harmless, tasty small dinosaurs may have mimicked these warning colors to take advantage of the notorious reputations of their look-alikes, a subterfuge practiced by modern butterflies, amphibians, and reptiles. Color was also probably used as a sexual attractant on crests, beaks, tails, wattles, and snouts. The fancy headgear on hadrosaurs certainly suggests sexual advertising, all the more effective in lime green and coral.

However, modern large birds, mammals, and reptiles are never gaily colored, sticking instead to basic browns, grays, tans, and greens. Probably large dinosaurs were conservative dressers, too. But they may have been patterned to assist them in camouflage like giraffes, tigers, and okapis. Dinosaurs lurking behind leaves may have had stripes or reticulated patterns of light and dark. Stripes baffle the eye on open grassland, so a zebra-striped dinosaur is a possibility. Babies may have had spots to help them blend into dappled shadows as lion and deer offspring do today. Like fish, aquatic reptiles most probably were light below and dark above to make them less visible to watery predators from below and flying predators from above. Similarly, early flying reptiles that fished along the shore probably wore basic shore-bird colors of gray above and white below for the same reason.

So most likely the inhabitants of subtropical forests and shores of the period were not dressed in the uniform tan we often imagine but sported patterns, spots, and stripes with bright crests and an occasional spot of

color. Although many older dinosaur displays depict creatures with gray or drab olive-green skin, newer museum dinosaurs are more colorful and much more animated because paleontologists have new ideas about dinosaurs.

Paleontologists also believe that dressing up for your girl was a dinosaur innovation; that's how they explain all the strange hats, helmets, and headgear worn by the beasts. *Dimetrodon,* who predated dinosaurs, was a pioneer in the apparel department. Before these fellows perked up the landscape, reptiles and amphibians kept a strictly low profile. Everyone ate meat and everyone was meat. *Dimetrodon* flashed his wicked set of carnivorous teeth and sported spiny sails across his back that not only made him seem bigger to his enemies and served as a solar heater to catch some rays, but also made him much more handsome to his mate. By the time hadrosaurs evolved, headgear to advertise for a mate included horns, crests, and various flaps of skin, probably decorated in bright colors. These dinosaurs had keen eyesight and hearing not only to keep them posted on the whereabouts of predators, but possibly also for checking out all the cute guys or gals in the area. Many dinosaurs also had variously modified air passages for making sounds; paleontologists believe these were for crooning lovesongs or trumpeting out triumph. The *Parasaurolophus* wore a six-foot trombone hooter; the thick-headed *Pachycephalosaurus* butted rivals head-on like a ram in rut. If paleontologists' guesses are correct, the chorus and percussion sections of the time must have been something to hear.

Skull of bone head dinosaur *Pachycephalosaur.* Courtesy Carter County Museum, Ekalaka, Montana.

Mammals Arrive on the Scene

The young mammoth had been grazing for several hours with the sun beating down on the light brown hair that sparsely covered his back. Small tusks protruded below his lower lip but his huge feet gave him the appearance of a young puppy with a lot of growing yet to do. Not far away, a gleaming patch of blue was visible through a small stand of trees. The pond promised a much-needed drink and a chance to wade right into the water for a shower. He began to graze away from the watchful eyes of his mother and aunts.

The youngster approached the pond cautiously, but after scanning the horizon and sniffing the air he gained the confidence to wander over to the shore. The water gently lapped the shoreline giving no clue to the pond's depth. Insects and a few leaves floated lazily on the pond's surface while several birds squawked noisily in the trees overhead.

The mammoth took a few steps into the water. The unusually warm mud oozed up in an unfamiliar way around his feet and made stepping somewhat difficult. A few more steps and the young animal began to struggle because he was sinking deeper into the black ooze that lined the bottom of the pond. Soon it was impossible for the terrified youngster to raise his legs. He trumpeted a frightened cry that boomed over the surrounding foothills.

The first animal to hear the terrified call was a lone and hungry Smilodon. The old saber-toothed cat was tired; she had not been successful in bringing down any prey for several days. The cat quickly altered her course and headed in the direction of the young mammoth's distress call. As she ascended a low hill just north, she saw the animal struggling in the pond. With no other thought but an easy dinner, the saber-tooth trotted down the hill and out into the pond.

In a moment, she too became trapped in the black ooze, which stuck to her fur-covered paws and drew her down. And, like the young mammoth, now sunken in the pond to his knees, the old cat forgot hunger and knew only fear.

The cries of the trapped mammoth became even more desperate. Finally, an answering trumpet came from beyond the grove of trees. The mother mammoth, traveling at a surprising speed for so large an animal, shouldered through the trees with a snapping and breaking of branches. Too wise to wade out in the dark, treacherous waters, the cow reached out with her long trunk and began to pull her offspring from the ooze, all the while uttering reassuring noises. Despite his frantic struggles, she managed to extricate one hind leg, then a second, and finally she hauled him out onto dry land, trembling, covered with tar, but safe.

The youngster immediately began to suckle for reassurance while his huge mother stood protectively over him on the edge of the pond, making crooning sounds. She pointedly ignored the plight of the mired cat some distance away. Saber-tooths were no match for healthy adult mammoths, but regularly preyed on the young, diseased, or infirm. An hour later, the only evidence that remained of the big saber-toothed cat's existence was a place on the pond where tiny bubbles of air popped on an otherwise calm surface. . . .

This mammoth appears caught in an Ice Age bog at the Cincinnati Museum of Natural History, Cincinnati, Ohio.

The most popular prehistoric mammals lived during the Pleistocene Epoch (see Chapter 3) and became extinct some ten or twelve thousand years ago. Many of them were large and exotic in comparison with the animals that roam North America today. Their large size has earned them the descriptive name *megafauna*. And despite the fact that collections of plastic prehistoric animal toys often contain a mixture of dinosaurs and megafauna, the two groups of animals were separated from one another by over 60 million years.

When we think of prehistoric mammals, we tend to think of the megafauna—mammoths, cave bears, and saber-tooths—which came along much later than dinosaurs. However, mammal-like reptiles evolved into the first true mammals at the same time reptiles were evolving into dinosaurs. The first small mammals tended to be overshadowed by the dinosaurs, which grew large and occupied the prominent daytime niches, while the small furry mammals lurked in the shadows and came out at night. It was not until dinosaurs became extinct that mammals came into the limelight as they grasped the great evolutionary opportunities in the dinosaurs' demise.

plains, the earliest horses were shy jungle dwellers (yes; there were jungles in North America) with the arched back and size of an alley cat that peeked from behind trees. Four padded toes insured jungle silence and an extra push for flight, but already there was a tiny thickened nail on the middle toe. Their teeth were adapted for eating fruit and juicy jungle plants. Gradually, their feet evolved to three toes and their teeth became larger and rounded for leaf eating. Horses were evolutionary pioneers, dashing from the protection of the forest to steal a mouthful of green grass. All that food in the open grasslands beckoned, and horses left the shadows for the sunlit prairie. Millions of years passed. Their legs grew longer and their feet spread into hooves; they could wheel and run at a moment's notice. Finally, in modern horses, the primitive outer toes have evolved into "splints" on either side of the hoof.

Scientists are much more comfortable with their reconstructions of prehistoric mammals than of dinosaurs because they have more and better fossils. The fossil record is much more complete both in specific detail and in providing clues for tracing evolutionary ties with the present and the past. When we deal with Pleistocene mammals that are in many ways very similar to animals that live today, we feel much more secure about our recreations of their lives.

For example, the evolution of the horse is written in a nearly complete fossil record of some 55 million years, spanning the history of mammalian evolution in the Cenozoic Period. Species branched out from a common ancestor. The progress from *Eohippus,* the dawn horse, includes *Mesohippus, Parahippus, Merychippus, Pliohippus,* and finally *Equus,* the Ice Age horse of the Great Plains and Texas, which traveled across the land bridges to other continents.

Twenty million years before they appeared on the

Grass responded to all this grazing by toughening with silica, so horses' teeth gradually flattened, hardened with enamel, and kept growing to replace wear. They modified to clippers and grinders. Jaws strengthened for lateral grinding of tough grains and plant stalks. Eyes moved laterally so their peripheral vision of predators improved. And horses joined the herd for additional protection.

Enormous horse herds lived on the plains of North America and migrated to the plains of Europe, Asia, Africa, and South America. Mysteriously, horses in the Western Hemisphere became extinct. There is no evidence that advancing glaciers, overpredation, disappearance of pasture, widespread epidemics, or competition was responsible. This evolutionary quirk is all the more puzzling when we remember how easily escaped European horses repopulated North and South America. Modern breeds are descended from extinct Asiatic horses and asses.

Larger than Life

One of the questions that has intrigued scientists most about dinosaurs and megafauna is not whether their skins were dusky brown or light gray, but why they were so *large* in comparison to their ancestors and the relatives that survived into the modern world. Some dinosaurs grew four stories tall and others were 70 feet long – or more. Mammoths, cave bears, early beavers, and many other Ice Age mammals also came in large, economy sizes. Why were they so big?

One theory holds that it's a matter of food supply and engineering. As long as the skeleton of an animal can support its body, its size is limited only by the amount of food available to it. In the lush pine forests of a hundred million years ago, large herbivorous dinosaurs dined on conifer needles constantly. The plants fought back: cycads toughened and covered themselves with spines (eventually new birdlike dinosaurs would evolve to eat these) and tall conifers shot up even taller. Over millions of years, tree trunks reached for the skies and dinosaur necks lengthened to overreach them. Finally *Apatosaurus* stood four stories tall and redwoods towered over him.

Body engineering began to limit dinosaur size. Even four supersturdy legs probably couldn't support more than ninety tons. Dinosaur skeletons evolved, becoming lighter and more streamlined, so although they were twenty times as large as a modern elephant, they did not weigh twenty times an elephant's weight. Their legs were unusually strong, and they may have spent some time in the water to help take a load off their feet.

When grassy plains provided unending food from horizon to horizon, large-sized mammals also evolved to take advantage of the food. Mammoths, ground sloths, beavers, elk, and others grew huge, and their predators – cave bears, lions, dire wolves, and saber-tooths – became enormous on the abundance of food.

But gigantic size ultimately proved to be a disadvantage in the quick-change environment of the Ice Age. Changes in global climate altered food supplies and the larger animals, slow to produce new generations of their kind, were unable to adapt quickly enough to survive.

Some of the most spectacular kinds of terrestrial mammals lived in North America during the last two million years – a period of time that was punctuated with many episodes of glaciation. Continent-sized ice sheets expanded and then receded over periods of tens of thousands of years in both hemispheres. While it is unambiguously true that people and dinosaurs did not meet one another, encounters between megafauna and man were not uncommon. The bones of mammoths, mastodons, and cave bears have turned up in prehistoric archaeological sites around the world. In addition, cave paintings in France, Spain, Italy, and other European countries attest not only to the extraordinary artistry of people who lived more than ten thousand years ago, but also to the important relationships that existed between early hunters and the large animals with whom they shared the prehistoric environment.

In our mind's eye, dinosaurs and megafauna are most memorable for their larger-than-life size. But another characteristic shared by both groups of animals is their rather sudden disappearance from the land-

scape. Paleontologists continue to be baffled by the extinction of these creatures (see Chapter 5). It's a puzzle that lends itself to conflicting theories and generates frequent controversy, and it's all part of our endless fascination for fossils.

Fossilized tree stump at Florissant Fossil Beds, Florissant, Colorado.

GRASS

Grass first appeared on the scene 50 million years ago. Until then the North American continent was an endless subtropical forest with the same weather report from coast to coast. When the undersea Pacific plate nudged the western edge of the continent, the Rocky Mountains began to jut up. Moist winds and mild showers that had previously swept across the Western Hemisphere were stopped dead from Alaska all the way to the tip of South America by the newly sprouting mountains. The weather report changed: winters turned cold and summers, hot and dry. Subtropical forests gave way to great plains. Similar changes took place on other continents. Trees died, grass grew, the food web changed, and animals evolved. Directly or indirectly, grass now feeds almost every land animal.

● Grass is not easy to eat. It provides only a tenth of its energy to the animals that eat it. With so much waste, grass-eating animals must spend all their days eating to get the nourishment they need. Munching on sand as well as tough grass stems, constantly grazing animals wore down their teeth. Animal evolution adapted with the ridged grinding teeth you can see in early horses, the sequential teeth of mammoths, and the continuously growing teeth of rodents.

● Grass is tough to digest. Ruminants developed double digestion systems, with a rumen to break down plant fiber before it enters the stomach. Most successful grass-eating animals, including giraffes, cattle, sheep, and goats, are ruminants. Birds swallowed pebbles to grind grass seeds in a special organ—the gizzard. Elephants extended their digestive systems so a meal of hay takes sixty hours from one end of the elephant to the other. Animals like the zebra, with neither a gizzard nor a rumen, spend most of their life head down, chewing. The zebra has twelve molars and an unusually large head to accommodate them.

● Grass provides little friendly cover. As the climate dried out, forests gave way to scattered trees and eventually to open prairie. Evolution ensured that animal legs grew longer and hooves evolved from toes for agility and fleetness of foot. Animals' necks stretched downward to reach the low grasses and upward to see above the tall grasses, and their eyesight and peripheral vision improved. Stripes, spots, and splotches that blended into the grass made them less obvious to predators— who in turn adopted the same camouflage techniques themselves.

● Grass grows not from the tip of the plant but from the base and spreads by seeds as well as by underground runners. As herds of animals developed and trampled competing bushes and shrubs, grass benefited. Herd movements guaranteed the spread of undigested seeds in droppings—with fertilizer right there; close-cropping teeth encouraged the underground spread of grass while killing shrubs and bushes. Herds—a hundred watching eyes, scenting nostrils, and listening ears—evolved to keep tabs on predators. Brains enlarged to cope with the social demands of living in a herd, and babies were strong enough to join the herd in flight almost from birth. Grass contributed to the rise of subfamilies of most modern animals, both herbivores and the carnivores that prey on them.

● Grass is cosmopolitan. Animals that can eat grass have a wide range of territory to choose from. Annual migration for breeding or to escape climate changes is possible for grazing animals, as grass grows in almost every habitat from alpine pastures to coastal mudflats, from tropical savannas to Antarctic islands. Grass evolved in Pangaea before the complete splitting up of continents and continued to grow and evolve as the modern continents took shape. Seeds carried by wind, birds, and mammals spread across the drifting land masses, and today as much as twenty percent of the Earth's land surface is dominated by grass.

3
A Question of Time

Painted Hills Unit, John Day Fossil Beds National Monument.

For a human being who might expect to live eighty or ninety years, a thousand years seems like a very long time indeed. Traveling back a thousand years — if that were possible — would take us to the medieval age of armored knights and ladies-in-waiting. Two thousand years would bring us to the Roman era with its emperors and legions, and five thousand years would carry us all the way back to the dawn of civilization. So, yes, a thousand years is a long time, but a million years last *a thousand times that long*. A hundred million years are ever so much longer, and a billion — a thousand thousand thousand — years is truly unimaginable. Yet these are the time spans that must be used to describe the history of life on Earth.

In 1642, prominent religious scholar Dr. John Lightfoot announced that he had determined the exact age of the earth — by reading the Bible. After painstaking analysis of the scriptures, he determined the planet's age to be a little less than 6,000 years. According to Lightfoot, the world was created on October 23, 4004 B.C. at nine o'clock in the morning. Modern scientists are not quite so precise as Lightfoot, and they

think in much larger units of time. Today, we think the earth has been in existence over four-and-one-half billion years. That is about 4.5 thousand-thousand-thousand years – 4,449,993,996 – longer than Lightfoot believed.

Over this truly colossal length of time, continents came together, broke apart, and drifted away. Massive ice sheets advanced and retreated again and again in both the northern and southern hemispheres, leaving in their wake dramatic landscape transformations. Primitive one-celled creatures' evolved into an array of life forms, as varied as snowflakes, as numerous as grains of sand on a beach – from green algae to sequoia, turtle to *Tyrannosaurus rex,* kangaroo rat to gorilla. As certain forms became extinct, others evolved to take their places. And only in relatively recent times, say the last 5 million years, have humans stepped onto the scene.

Scientists use events like these, which left traces behind in the earth, to partition our planet's history into smaller, more manageable units of time. So we chart major events against the giant yardstick of the geologic time scale, which consists of four *eras:*

> The Cenozoic (from 10,000 years ago to 60 million years ago)
> The Mesozoic (from 60 to 225 million years ago)
> The Paleozoic (from 225 to 600 million years ago)
> The Precambrian (everything earier than 600 million years ago)

Scientists divide these major eras into *periods* which are further subdivided into *epochs.* For example, dinosaurs evolved and became extinct during the three Mesozoic periods: the Triassic, the Jurassic, and the Cretaceous. No dinosaur species lived throughout the Mesozoic Era. The toothy *Tyrannosaurus rex* prowled

This butterfly, *Prodryas persephone*, once fluttered above the lake at Florissant Fossil Beds, Colorado.

North America at about the same time its smaller but nonetheless ferocious cousin *Tarbosaurus* roamed Mongolia, but many millions of years *after* the scelidosaurs, with their formidable spikes, ambled about England. Although mammals first appeared in the Triassic, the extinct mammals that catch our attention—the big ones like mastodons—flourished during the Quaternary Period from about 10,000 to 2 million years ago.

Getting a Date

How do we determine the ages of these events? Prehistoric animals left no calendars behind, so how can we know whether a fossilized bone is 50,000 or 100 million years old? The answer is that we never know precisely. But scientists can establish the age of a find with reasonable confidence by using either or both of two widely accepted methods known as *relative dating* and *absolute dating*. Relative dating is the most commonly used technique for determining the age of a fossil.

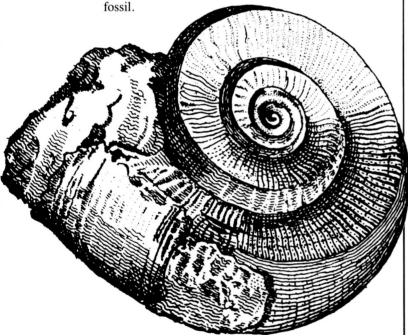

Our planet's history is preserved in distinct layers of rock and soil, and the layers often vary in color or texture or in the type of rock they contain. These differences can be seen quite clearly on the sides of the cliffs at the Parc de Miguasha in Quebec (see page 57) or on the wall of fossils in the Dinosaur Quarry at Dinosaur National Monument in Utah (see page 86). They can even be seen alongside highways where construction crews have blasted and bulldozed through several layers representing millions of years of earth history. But the deepest cut in the earth is not man-made; it was carved out by a river. The Grand Canyon is more than a mile deep, and as you hike down toward the Colorado River at the bottom of the canyon, you'll see dozens, even hundreds of colorful layers. Before you reach the river, you will travel through 2,000 *million* years of fossil history.

Whether in a road cut or the Grand Canyon, the oldest layers are usually at the bottom. It is this fact that makes relative dating possible. Although relative dating doesn't tell us the exact age in years of an old bone found in an upper layer, it does allow us to assume the bone is younger than another fossil pulled from a lower level. That is how paleontologists know the horned *Triceratops* lived long before the elephant-like wooly mammoth: the fossilized remains of the *Triceratops* are found in much lower layers.

Over the last forty years, scientists have discovered several dating methods that allow them to assign absolute rather than relative dates to prehistoric events and finds. Having learned that unstable forms of elements such as carbon and potassium decay radioactively at constant and specific rates, scientists have devised methods of using these elements and rates to determine the ages of prehistoric samples. By multiplying the known rate of decay by the quantity of the element left in a sample, they can calculate its age.

For example, the element carbon occurs in several forms including an unstable variety called carbon-14 or radiocarbon. All living organisms, both animals and plants, absorb carbon-14 as they breathe in carbon dioxide from the air. When they die, respiration ceases and no more carbon-14 enters their bodies. The carbon-14 trapped in the body begins to decay and half of it is gone after 5,568 years. Half of the remaining half decays after another 5,568 years. Since we can measure the amount of carbon-14 left in an old bone or piece of wood, we can calculate how old it is. The radiocarbon system is not foolproof, and is currently useful only for dating organisms that lived during the past 75,000 years. But as the method is refined, scientists may be able to extend the reach of its measurements to more than 100,000 years.

Female Ammonite.

(Right) Layers of rock with fossils show up clearly in this exhibit at the California Academy of Sciences in San Francisco. Photo by Susan Middleton.

The decay of potassium into argon gas can be used to date materials that are many millions of years old. However, it can only be used to date certain types of *rock,* not the fossils in the rock. Scientists use it to date the volcanic rocks found above or below the fossil, and this enables them to approximate its age.

Both relative dating and absolute dating contribute to our knowledge about the past, and sometimes these methods are used together. If two fossils look alike — even if they come from different parts of the world — it can be assumed they were left by organisms that lived at about the same time. If an absolute date can be determined for one specimen, it provides an approximate age for the other specimen.

The Petrified Creatures Museum in Richfield Springs, New York (see page 54), contains another important tool for scientists. The museum's collection of 400-million-year-old (Devonian) sea creatures are considered "index fossils." As such they are used to "cross date" Devonian finds from all over the world.

Paleontologists, archaeologists, geologists, and other scientists who do research in different parts of the globe use these index fossils to approximate the ages of their finds.

It is important to remember that researchers still have much to learn about the history of the earth, especially in dating specific events like when certain creatures lived or became extinct. But our ability to date these events improves continuously, and perhaps tomorrow's techniques will make today's seem primitive.

Since the intervals of prehistoric time are so large and the methods of measurement inexact, you will occasionally find discrepancies in dates given in books or in museum displays. One exhibit may label the end of the Age of Dinosaurs at 70 million years ago while another lists it as 65 million years ago. While a difference of 5 million years may seem enormous, it really isn't. Relatively speaking, a 5-million-year error is small when seen against the vast backdrop of prehistory.

THE ICE AGE

In 1837, after studying certain polished rocks and geological deposits, American naturalist Louis Agassiz formulated the idea of an ice age. Initially he conceived of it as a single cold period, but we now know that over the last 1.5 million years of Earth's history, there was a *succession* of great glaciations when almost all of northern North America was covered in ice. This was the Pleistocene Epoch.

But the Pleistocene was not an endless winter. Glaciers waxed and waned so that climate swung between cold and warm. In America, the glacial periods are named after the states where the best evidence of them has been found. From oldest to

east. Over time, these animals gradually moved south to populate the Western Hemisphere. The Panama land bridge linking North and South America enabled animals such as horses, squirrels, mammoths, wolves, and saber-toothed cats to travel south while opossums, armadillos, and porcupines traveled north.

Around the world, as glaciers spread down from the north, species were forced south. On some continents, east–west mountain ranges and other barriers trapped animals which then became extinct with the advance of the glaciers. But because North America has mountain chains that run north and south, animals were able to migrate south ahead of

youngest, the glaciations are called Nebraskan (which began about 1.5 million years ago), Kansas, Illinoian, and Wisconsin.

The water to make all that glacial ice came from the oceans, lowering them considerably and creating broad land bridges between continents. Beringa, a bridge a thousand miles wide, joined Siberia to Alaska and allowed old world animals to migrate

the glaciers. There are no land barriers until the Gulf of Mexico, so many animals moved to the southern United States (or even South America) to escape the cold. Thus Florida, Arizona, Texas, and other southern states have some of the richest Pleistocene records in the world, and North America has a wide variety of species unknown elsewhere in the Northern Hemisphere.

Winter snow creates an Ice Age landscape at Badlands National Park, South Dakota.

4
Finding & Figuring Out Fossils

Paleontologists apply the term *fossil* to the mineralized, cell-by-cell replacement of soft tissue and other body parts of organisms that lived long ago. So precise is this replacement that paleontologists can trace the marks of delicate nerve tissue on fossilized dinosaur skulls. But turning wood, skin, or bone to stone is a rare natural process that takes a long time, and conditions must be just right.

First, a plant or animal must die where it can be buried rapidly. Unless the remains are quickly placed out of reach, decomposition and scavengers put an end to fossilization before it starts. The process of fossilization can take hundreds and even thousands of years to complete, and most body parts consist of soft tissue that rarely survives long enough for this to occur. Bones, however, resist destruction and last for a longer

time than skin or organs—which is why the fossil record of dinosaurs and mammals consists mostly of bones.

Second, the area where the bones are buried must contain minerals dissolved in water percolating through the ground in contact with the corpse. Any increase in the presence of ground water could dilute the concentrations of minerals and slow fossilization. Or the drying out of an area could stop the fossilization process completely.

The third condition is that the grave area must remain undisturbed and unchanged so that fossilization can go on uninterrupted. Good caches of fossils often turn up in caves or sinkholes, safe from disturbances. For example, at the Mammoth Site in Hot Springs, South Dakota (page 75), the fossils of more than 100

(Left) Runoff from melting ice splashes visitors' faces in the Ice Age exhibit at the Cincinnati Museum of Natural History, Cincinnati, Ohio.

Diplancanthys etched in the rock at Parc de Miguasha, Quebec. Photo by Fred Klus.

individual animals have been excavated from a huge sinkhole.

Good areas for fossils to form include swamps, stagnant ponds, and ocean bottoms where the muddy sediments are left undisturbed. However, environments change so much through time that today's swamps and stagnant ponds are not likely to be the locations of the swamps and stagnant ponds of long ago. Even an active imagination finds it difficult to believe that lakes or wetlands once covered the badlands of Montana or Wyoming. In fact, many of our most spectacular fossil finds come from areas that today are very dry. Museum creations of the places where Cretaceous dinosaurs roamed and Pleistocene mammals grazed often depict water because evidence indicates that water was present during those periods.

In addition to fossilized bone, there are many other kinds of remains that can inform us about ancient animals and their lives. Occasionally, for instance, the frozen remains of a mammoth are recovered. There is at least one story about the frozen flesh of a mammoth find being so fresh that dogs scavenged the carcass before it could be salvaged for study. Discovery of frozen animals, and rarely even frozen people, are important because the preserved hair, skin, muscles, organs, stomach contents, and even blood can tell us much more about the animal than we can learn from fossilized bone.

Drying is very similar to freezing in that it preserves soft tissue for long periods of time. Mummies are a familiar example, and they can occur outside the tombs of ancient pharaohs. For example, in the arid southwestern United States, the dried-out, naturally mummified remains of people, plants, and animals such as birds, reptiles, and amphibians have been uncovered. The American Museum of Natural History even has a fossil of a mummified duckbilled dinosaur from Wyoming with some of its skin still intact. Finds like these give us a more detailed—and sometimes startling—glimpse into the past that fossilized bones cannot.

Sometimes the evidence uncovered about prehistoric animals is indirect, and dinosaur footprints are a good example. Just as your bare feet leave impressions in the wet sand at the water's edge, so did dinosaur and mammal feet millions of years ago. With climatic and geological changes, the sand and mud where the prints

were made slowly dried out, were covered by more sand and mud, and—left undisturbed for thousands of years—finally turned to stone. These stone footprints give us clues to a creature's size, weight, and walking habits, whether it stood on four legs or two, was fleeing a predator or out for a stroll, was solitary or en-

joyed a social life. You can see dinosaur footprints in many museums and parks such as Dinosaur State Park in Connecticut (page 48) and Dinosaur Valley State Park in Texas (page 61).

A cast is another form of indirect evidence. While a dinosaur's footprint is not a very detailed mold because wet sand or mud tumbled in around the track after the dinosaur made it, the details of the inside of a clam or snail shell can become perfectly cast when sediment enters the shell and remains undisturbed. Slowly the resistant shell decays and the sediments on the inside solidify. Eventually all the shell erodes away leaving behind a perfect stone replica of its inside surface.

A Challenging Job

Initially, fossil collecting efforts concentrated on finding desirable specimens in often exotic places and packing them out for view in privates homes and museums. The more spectacular discoveries—the huge creatures with movie-monster qualities—were reassembled in prominent places to impress the ever-curious public. The less glamorous discoveries were often left in unopened crates and relegated to museum basements, where some still remain today.

(Above) Paleontologists painstakingly expose fossilized bones in the Quarry at Dinosaur National Monument, Jensen, Utah, where more than 2,200 such specimens have turned up.

(Right) This *Torosaurus* skeleton is still in its plaster traveling jacket at the Milwaukee Public Museum in Wisconsin.

During the early days of American and Canadian fossil dinosaur and mammal collecting, many exciting discoveries were made across North America. Nineteenth and early twentieth century paleontologists concerned themselves mostly with what dinosaurs and prehistoric mammals looked like, how they were related to one another, and what they ate. Retrieving fossilized bones was the essential task of fieldwork because it was the bones that spoke to paleontologists about what they wanted to learn.

These early scientists devoted a lot of time to describing and classifying prehistoric animals. No one worried whether the places where fossils were found were the places where the actual prehistoric animal had lived and died. And most scholars did not question if two bones found together were really deposited together at the same time – or even came from the same animal. The answers to these questions were taken for granted, and interesting but erroneous interpretations of dinosaur behavior and body forms resulted. For example, it took seventy years for the *Brontosaurus* at the Carnegie Museum to receive the correct head: it was originally fitted with a *Camarasaurus* skull found several miles away because a single *Camarasaurus*

tooth had been found with the rest of the *Brontosaurus* skeleton.

Modern paleontological field studies involve much more than locating and carefully removing fossilized bones for display. No longer do paleontologists remain in their comfortable laboratories back East while fieldworkers comb the western deserts and mountains, braving Indian attack, grizzly bears, snow, heat, and biting insects, to haul out huge dinosaur skeletons by mule to the nearest rail head for shipment to Philadelphia, New Haven, New York, or Pittsburgh. Nowadays, collecting individual fossil specimens is only a small portion of the fieldwork, and today's paleontologist in the field concentrates on careful study of the *context* and *history* of the fossils.

Classifying and studying dinosaur remains is still very important, but accurately understanding how the animals lived and died depends on knowing what has happened to their remains since death. This area of study is called *taphonomy* and it is an essential part of paleontological and archaeological field research today. Taphonomy involves documenting the histories of fossils, including the many possible disturbances to the remains between the time the animal died and the

time the paleontologist gets out the shovel or rock hammer.

Vultures carrying off part of the remains and coyotes gnawing on the bones or burying them for a later snack are examples of *biological* disturbances. Activities like these determine whether a bone can even become a fossil and may explain why many small, portable bones are often missing from fossilized dinosaur skeletons. It is very rare to find a carcass that has not been scavenged, and paleontologists must reconstruct the missing bones by comparing them with other similar dinosaurs. So although many of the dinosaur skeletons you see on display appear to be whole, it is likely that parts of them have been made with plaster and fiberglass.

Geological activity also greatly influences what fossils are available for study. Earthquakes and volcanoes can either preserve or destroy relatively complete fossil skeletons. Recently Chinese and Canadian paleontologists unearthed a nest of fossilized baby

ankylosaurs in Mongolia that had been buried beneath a sand slide. Prehistoric animals that died near rivers can have their carcasses washed downstream during floods. Water transport can also combine the bones of several animals creating some very strange "riverbed-fellows": live animals that would never be caught dead with each other *are!*

Geologic processes not only shape the fossil record but also expose that record to us. As rivers cut new courses and rock layers shift through time, very old rock layers get exposed at the ground surface for scientific inspection. Erosion aids paleontological research on a larger, much wider scale than bulldozers do; many of the greatest paleontological discoveries would not have been made without its assistance, as fossil-bearing layers would have remained too deeply buried for uncovering by human effort alone.

Finally, *cultural activity* makes its mark on the fossil record. The construction of roads and industrial parks can obliterate fossils that go unobserved from a

No wonder it's hard to tell which bone goes where. An ancient river scatters dinosaur bones while scavenger dinosaurs dine. Courtesy Dinosaur National Monument, Jensen, Utah.

bulldozer seat—or it can uncover new finds: the mammoth at the Bergen County Museum (page 49) turned up when New Jersey roads were being repaired. Amateur collectors may unknowingly cause great damage to fossil locations by not carefully excavating and recording their discoveries. And even paleontologists themselves, by excavating holes into fossil-bearing rock layers, partially destroy the fossil record for future scientists to examine. On the whole, however, they very meticulously record and remove their discoveries from the ground, realizing only too well that there are no more dinosaurs or mammoths to become fossils. Once they are all dug up, there will be no new discoveries to unearth.

Digging for Dinosaurs

Finding fossils is no small task. Today's environments do not necessarily resemble the environments of long ago, so where do we look? Many fossil-bearing rocks are buried under thousands of feet of other rocks and sediments; how do we get to them? And fossilization itself is an extremely rare process, so what are our chances of actually finding what we're looking for?

Quite frankly, a lot of important fossil collecting locations have been discovered with a combination of luck and educated guesswork. Some of the best areas to begin hunting for fossils are regions where geologic uplifting and erosion expose millions of years of rocks and sediments. Shales and slates, formed from fine-grained particles at one time saturated with water, provide favorable conditions for fossilization. Conversely, hot volcanic rocks such as basalt and granite would usually have destroyed any animal remains they came in contact with.

Today paleontologists have many kinds of information—and some interesting new technologies such as ground-penetrating radar and satellite imagery—to aid their search for fossils. Once they locate the fossil beds and determine that they are useful for research, the long and arduous task of recovery begins.

A vast collection of field methods and equipment similar to those employed by archaeologists are used on dinosaur digs. The paleontologist's first step is to divide the site into equal-sized squares so that information can be collected and identified from precisely defined units of earth. A reference or datum point is placed off the site to mark the location and provide a basis for taking elevations. Then the scientists use surveying equipment to make a detailed map of the area. Paleontologists dig carefully excavated holes documented with page after page of field notes; nothing is left unrecorded. An on-site computer may be used to record and manipulate data. Questions posed and answered are endless. What was the condition of the bone? Was it near any other specimen? What was the soil or rock around it like? How deeply was it buried? How was the bone oriented? Will it be difficult to remove? And on and on.

But fieldwork is much more than answering questions. Each site and each find presents unique logistical problems in uncovering, removing, and transporting the often fragile fossils. For example, at sinkhole sites—which consist of large, deep bell-shaped or bottle-shaped caverns with relatively small openings at the ground surface—the fossils may lie exposed on the cavern floor, easily accessible at first, and the problem may be how to transport them safely up and out for closer examination in the field or museum lab. At erosion sites such as riverbanks and arroyos, great

amounts of earth or rock must first be removed before the delicate task of uncovering the fossils can begin.

Even though fossilized bones have turned to stone, they are often very fragile—more brittle than the stone surrounding them—so they require extremely careful

Bone preservation at the Mammoth Site of Hot Springs. Photo by Rushmore Photos. Courtesy of the Mammoth Site of Hot Springs, South Dakota.

treatment. Uncovering and removing fossil remains that have been embedded in stone is so time-consuming at the site that most of the detailed work takes place later in the laboratory. In the lab, hundreds of patient hours can be spent with magnifying glasses and small dental instruments just picking and chipping away at the stone encasing a jaw fragment or leg bone.

Once freed from their rock tombs, the fossils often must be coated with special adhesives to keep them from falling apart. Then, to protect them during transport, plaster casts similar to those used on broken arms or legs may be applied. Such casts have been in use since the horse-and-buggy days because they can be quickly put on in the field and then removed at leisure back at the museum.

Unique, permanent catalog numbers are attached to each specimen to relate it to the catalog of previously collected information on the fossil.

After initial study, the majority of fossils end up in museum storage, where they are carefully packed away until other scientists come along to study them. But for a few special fossils, the journey continues out of the laboratory and into the limelight for public viewing. These specimens are truly the rarest because they include only the very best-preserved fossils.

Preparing fossils for public display requires artistry and ingenuity, and utilizes the specialized talents of many dedicated people. Assembling fossilized bones to reconstruct a dinosaur skeleton involves scientists who understand how the bones once fitted together, engineers to figure out how to keep the bones connected and suspended in midair, and artists to fill in the gaps where pieces of bone are missing altogether. And because the most spectacular specimens are also the most rare, museums often must rely on casts of fossilized bones for display rather than the real thing. After all, there are only a handful of *T. rex* skeletons to go around.

Face to face at the Carnegie Museum of Natural History.

Some museums—like the Mammoth Site at Hot Springs, the Tyrrell in Alberta, Canada (page 91), the Denver Museum of Natural History (page 81), and the George Page Museum at La Brea Tar Pits in southern California (page 79)—can give you an on-site sense of what fieldwork and paleontology lab work are all about. Books also provide some valuable information. However, participating in a dig yourself is the best and most enjoyable way to learn how fossil sites are excavated and information unearthed. In the "Dinosaur Digs" chapter later in this book we provide a list of field opportunities for amateurs. What we can promise you is that fieldwork requires a great deal of patience. It means getting along with others in the field when it's hot and dry and a refreshing shower is only a dream, or where mosquitoes outnumber paleontologists ten million to one. It requires attention to minute detail and careful record-keeping despite the fact that all you uncovered in your pit yesterday was the tiny toe bone of some extinct animal whose name you can't pronounce. On the other hand, working on a dig can be extremely exciting and rewarding. After all, yours could be the dig that brings to light an important new discovery. . . .

MAKING A LIFE-SIZED DINOSAUR MODEL

Have you ever wondered who made the large dinosaur models like those in Dinosaur Valley State Park in Texas? How did the artist accomplish this monumental task?

Well, the Texas models of *Brontosaurus* and *Tyrannosaurus rex* were built by New York artist Louis Paul Jonas for the Sinclair Oil Exhibit at the 1964–65 World's Fair. Jonas began by making hundreds of small models and sketches of the two dinosaurs. Eventually he settled on a single, detailed clay model of each animal, one-tenth its actual size. He photographed his dinosaur models and projected the photographs onto huge pieces of wallboard, adjusting the pictures until they were exactly lifesized. Tracing around the pictures, he then cut the wallboard into two-dimensional dinosaurs.

Next, Jonas stretched screening around the wallboard cutouts, adding burlap and plaster to create a fleshed-out, three-dimensional shape. Then he added several tons of modeling clay and sculpted the skin texture, and facial features like eyes and teeth. When the clay had dried, Jonas cut up each dinosaur—the *Brontosaurus* required eighty-six pieces—and used each piece to make plaster molds. Into these molds, he poured a mixture of fiberglass and polyester resin. When the plastic set, he bolted the resulting pieces of dinosaur to special frames of paper tubes filled with concrete. After filling and smoothing the seams, he sandblasted, washed, and painted the skin, and the two huge dinosaurs stood there in his studio looking just as they had 180 million years ago.

Much to the delight of New Yorkers, the dinosaurs floated on barges down the Hudson River to Flushing Meadows, where they starred in the World's Fair before moving on to Texas and further triumphs.

Paleontologist from the American Museum of Natural History digging dinosaurs in China.

Large-as-life *Stegosaurus* greets Quarry visitors at Dinosaur National Monument in Utah.

5
Extinction:
Where'd They Go?

For many of us, the mystery of dinosaur and mega-fauna extinction is as fascinating as their great size. Why would such strong, enormous creatures simply die out? What on Earth could have happened to pre-cipitate their sudden demise? Such questions have plagued scientists for nearly two centuries, and con-troversy still rages. Over the years, more than ninety theories of extinction have been advanced . . . and paleontologists have yet to agree on just one.

Extinction Is Forever

Extinction is the total elimination of an animal or plant species, and it is not reversible. Easily traceable through the fossil record from the earliest times to the present, extinction is the ultimate fate of most animals and plants. In fact, an estimated 98% of all species that have ever lived on Earth are now extinct. The road to extinction is a natural path from the initial evolution of a species, through its growth and flourishing, to its eventual disappearance. The extinction process itself begins when a particular plant or animal is no longer successful in passing its genetic heritage on to the next generation. Gradually, or sometimes catastrophically, fewer and fewer members of the species survive until finally there are so few remaining that no offspring are produced. Most species survive one to two million years and then die out. If they are replaced by a

daughter species, one directly descended, they are con-sidered an evolutionary success.

In 1812, French naturalist Georges Cuvier first for-mulated the theory of extinction—a radical departure from the widely accepted Biblical idea that Creation took place once, for always, during the famous seven days in Genesis. Long before Darwin's ideas on the continual origin of species were conceived and pub-lished, Cuvier realized that the fossil specimens he was studying were of species no longer living. Examining some 120 fossils from the Seine basin, he discovered ninety of them had no living counterparts. Cuvier con-ceived the novel idea that extinction is the fate of all species, and like some paleontologists today, he blamed extinction on cycles of catastrophes.

Many factors can influence the speed with which extinction occurs. Predators moving into a new en-vironment can quickly eliminate a prey species that has not evolved defensive behaviors or mechanisms such as hard shells or other kinds of body armor to ward off attacks. For example, land bridges that allowed the free migration of species from one continent to another introduced competing plant eaters and formidable predators like cave lions. As these new herbivores and predators moved south across the Panama land bridge into South America, most of the South American hoofed herbivores gradually became extinct—the vic-tims of predation and competition for food.

Changes in the environment can favor one species over another and result in changes throughout the food web, first in vegetation, then in the herbivores and car-nivores. For example, volcanoes or rising mountain ridges create or alter river flood plains. When new lush vegetation spreads along the river, herbivores come for the juicy plants and carnivores for the juicy herbivores. Species unable to adapt to these changes in food and

The Texas-sized armadillo at the Houston Museum of Natural Science.

This fierce *Allosaurus* roamed Utah 140 million years ago. Courtesy Dinosaur National Monument.

(Pages 36-37) Did man contribute to the extinction of prehistoric mammals? Courtesy of Utah Museum of Natural History.

predation die out, and empty niches in the ecosystem are soon filled by new species that *can* adapt.

Human activity can and has significantly contributed to speeding and slowing the extinction process. Hunting bison on the Great Plains and musk-oxen in Canada during the nineteenth century almost caused the extinction of these two species. But fortunately, a developing awareness of the implications of overhunting saved them both.

Sorting out which influences are responsible for the extinction of any single species or group of animals is difficult at best because there are so many different processes that can be involved. It is not surprising then to learn that paleontologists often come up with conflicting ideas to explain why certain animals permanently disappeared from the fossil record. Scientific controversy surrounds the disappearance of both the dinosaurs and Pleistocene mammals.

No single theory has been unanimously adopted to account for what happened to the dinosaurs about 65 million years ago. What is clear is that fifty to sixty percent of *all* fauna — not just dinosaurs — disappeared at the end of the Cretaceous Period. In North America to date, the best known dinosaurs were discovered as fossils in Hell Creek, Montana. *Tyrannosaurus rex, Triceratops,* small birdlike dinosaurs, and armored dinosaurs were the last of the "terrible lizards" to walk the earth. Some non-dinosaurs — pterosaurs, plesiosaurs, mosasaurs, nautilus-like ammonites, and plankton — also died out while others survived: turtles, lizards, crocodiles, birds, small mammals, and insects such as dragonflies, ants, and cockroaches. Whatever caused dinosaur extinction did not wipe out everything, and many mysteries remain along with the creatures that survived.

The Case of the Disappearing Dinosaurs

If we stepped into a time machine and zoomed back 65 million years, it is unlikely we could set the dial to stop so we could watch the day the dinosaurs died. It may have taken more than a million years for the dinosaurs to disappear or it may have required no more than a few decades. Because our ability to date the end of the Cretaceous Period is not very refined, it is im-

possible to know exactly how long it took all of the major groups of dinosaurs to become extinct. Yet it is important to know how long dinosaur extinction took because different lengths of time are linked to different theories of extinction.

One school of paleontology argues that the extinction of the dinosaurs was a slow process that resulted in their gradual replacement by fur-bearing, milk-producing, placental mammals that were more successful in adapting to gradually lowering temperatures. You may see paintings or diagrams in some of the museums you visit that depict small, shrewlike mam-

mals sneaking into dinosaur nests to steal eggs. This idea is based on the ecological principle of the food web: if one part of the web is interrupted, then other parts of the web will experience consequences as well. In this line of reasoning, as climate became cooler and habitat disappeared, so did some of the dinosaurs. Additionally, since some of these dinosaurs were important prey species for other dinosaurs, their dwindling numbers shrank the food supply for the predatory dinosaurs. Eventually there were so few prey species left that other dinosaurs who depended on them for food also died out.

Another theory holds that some particularly lethal virus or disease evolved that infected and killed off the dinosaurs, an idea supported by observations of viruses and diseases causing massive die-offs of animals, including people, in relatively recent times (for example, the bubonic plague of medieval Europe or influenza in 1918). Viruses tend to be relatively fast-acting, and the virus-theory paleontologists thought the fossil record demonstrated that dinosaur extinction took place rapidly at the end of the Cretaceous Period. Whatever the virus may have been, paleontologists argued it only

affected the dinosaurs and cleared the way for mammals to evolve into the many niches left open by their disappearance. This theory is not as popular as it used to be.

The theory that has gained the most widespread acceptance in recent years is that dinosaur extinction was the consequence of a catastrophic event that occurred on a global scale and permanently altered the course of Earth's history. This theory dates all the way back to Georges Cuvier's initial theory of extinction, but finding the proof to support it has been somewhat elusive until recently.

Global-catastrophe thinking goes that about 65 million years ago a huge meteorite collided with the earth with such impact that it altered worldwide weather patterns. Fantastically huge tidal waves pounded coastlines and enormous amounts of dust and water vapor filled the atmosphere. In the years following the devastating collision, massive die-offs of plants and animals took place, but for some reason mammals were less susceptible than dinosaurs. In fact, the theory goes, mammals actually benefited from the cataclysm and moved rapidly into the ecological niches vacated by dinosaurs.

For a long time, paleontologists have searched for evidence of a meteoritic impact large enough to cause such astounding consequences. A rare earth mineral called iridium had been noticed in Late Cretaceous deposits around the globe, strongly hinting at an extraterrestrial collision, but no site for the impact had been confidently identified. For a while, Hudson Bay was thought to be a likely candidate. More recently, geological survey work involving satellite photography has revealed a new possibility off the Yucatan Peninsula of Mexico. In this case, corroborative evidence exists in the form of iridium, shocked quartz, and tiny pieces of fused, natural glass called tektites. Tektites would have formed when enormous heat generated by the meteorite striking the earth melted certain rocks around the impact area and fused them into glass. Ironically, these tiny bits of glass may contain the answer to one of our planet's most monumental mysteries.

Although more than ninety already exist, perhaps yet another theory will be advanced that better explains the demise of the dinosaurs. Or it may be that a combination of theories will finally account for dinosaur extinctions better than any single one. As we learn more

Excavating a skull of Varanoid lizard in Mongolia. Courtesy American Museum of Natural History.

about how to date the past, a clearer picture of the time involved in the extinction of the dinosaurs will help paleontologists to decide what ultimately happened to these animals whose spectacular size and diversity not only dominated a large chunk of Earth's history, but also captured the imagination of people for almost two centuries of scientific inquiry. One thing is for certain, however: dinosaurs were an immensely successful group of animals who dominated the living world for about 135 million years. During that time, dinosaurs shaped the course of evolution, and their disappearance *set* the course of evolution for the next 65 million years.

Marvelous, Mysterious Megafauna

Dinosaurs' demise opened up great new evolutionary opportunities for mammals, and like their predecessors, mammals quickly diversified and expanded into virtually every environmental niche on Earth. Theirs is a success story that continues to unfold with no end in sight. Along the way, however, various species have arisen and then fallen by the evolutionary wayside—among them much of the megafauna of the Pleistocene Epoch. The fantastic mammals that we have come to associate with the prehistoric period—mammoths, mastodons, wooly rhinos, huge cave bears, and saber-toothed cats—did not survive into the modern age (though some of their cousins are still with us). Explanations for their extinction are as varied as those for the disappearance of the dinosaurs, but some are quite similar—the weather changed, a disease spread rapidly showing no mercy. But one explanation

sets itself apart from those used to talk about dinosaur extinction because it includes an important element that wasn't present 65 million years ago: people.

North America was home to many huge and somewhat exotic-appearing mammals by today's standards. Enormous and powerful buffalo roamed the grass-covered plains that extended from Texas in the south to western Canada in the north. Elephants with magnificent curving tusks grazed and foraged from one side of the continent to the other. Great cats with extraordinarily well-developed canine teeth preyed on herds of horses and other grass-eating species. But sometime around 10,000 years ago, all of these remarkable creatures vanished from the landscape. Paleontologists and archaeologists have been fascinated by this seemingly abrupt departure. This episode of Pleistocene extinction has received considerable study and has created plenty of controversy because for the first time human beings are implicated in the extinction of species.

The argument goes something like this. Beringa, a huge land bridge connecting North America with Asia via Siberia, existed during the Pleistocene Period. This vast land mass allowed for the migration of animals between the two continents. During the last ice age, some 15,000 years ago, *people* from Asia also migrated into North America. (Some hunting and gathering people may have migrated into the New World during an earlier glacial period but most of the evidence for them is somewhat in doubt.) As the new migrants made their way into North America, they discovered an abundance of food—both animal and vegetable. Some archaeologists have argued that not only was food abundant, it was extremely easy to obtain. They conclude that large late Pleistocene animals were easy prey to human hunters who had an efficient technology to

(Left) Thirty million years ago this saber-toothed cat stalked prey in Nebraska. Courtesy Houston Museum of Natural Science.

(Below) A saber-toothed cat and her cubs, a new generation of fearsome Ice Age predators. Courtesy Cincinnati Museum of Natural History.

kill them. The hunters were many times more successful at bringing down mammoths and mastodons than their wild predator counterparts, so eventually large herbivores and the carnivores that had hunted them became extinct.

Once again, it is very difficult to pinpoint the dates of extinction and to be sure that the very last bones of a species have been found. Dung — which large herbivores produced much more copiously than bones in the course of their lives — has been well-preserved in the caves of arid areas and can be dated. Fossilized dung indicates the lumbering ground sloth was last seen in

the American southwest about 11,000 years ago, the time we think hunting humans arrived in the area. In essence, the argument goes, the New World immigrants of 12,000 to 15,000 years ago were largely successful at eating themselves out of house and home.

However, most scholars today believe that the major causes of megafauna extinction were brought on by the termination of the last ice age. While the reasons for the end of it remain unclear, all kinds of prehistoric environmental evidence show that the landscape was massively transformed by the retreating ice sheets. The climate warmed; tundra and grasslands were replaced

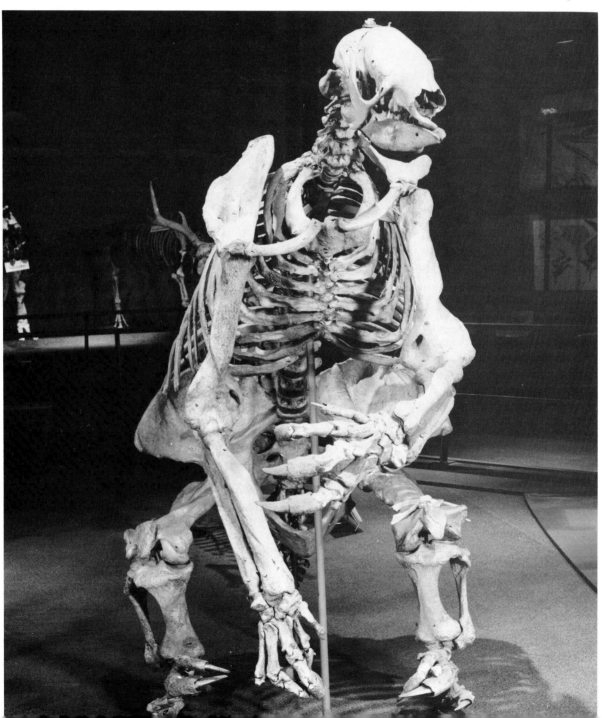

in many regions by parkland and forest. Animals that had once thrived in the cool, open environments were replaced by other species that were adapted to warmer, more wooded conditions. It's hard to imagine an open-tundra animal like the giant Irish elk with its 12-foot antler span managing to escape predators running through the forest. It is also possible that climate and environmental changes made these animals more sensitive to pressures like human hunting. In any event, tundra animals such as the wooly rhinoceros, wooly mammoth, cave bear, and Irish elk died out.

Some of the museum exhibits that you'll inevitably encounter will depict a group of hunters armed with sharp stone-tipped spears in the process of dispatching a mammoth. Kill sites like this have been uncovered by archaeologists in many places from Mexico to Canada. People may indeed have played a role in speeding the process of extinction for certain species, like mammoths, that they depended on for food. However, human hunting alone was probably not the primary cause of the mammoths' disappearance in North America, Europe, or anywhere else at the end of the last ice age.

You don't need to be a scholar to appreciate fossils of dinosaurs and megafauna. All you need is an open mind for new ideas and a vivid imagination to fill in details where words leave gaps. Our understanding of the past is always being modified to accommodate new discoveries — those made in the ground and those made in the minds of people who devote their lives to studying it. Museums provide the essential repositories for keeping and protecting important records of the past for all of us to enjoy and for a few of us to study. Some of our most important discoveries have come not from new excavations but from examination of already collected specimens using different theoretical perspectives. For example, the modern dinosaur wears a much more beautifully colored skin than his counterpart of only twenty-five years ago — as a result of new ideas, not new fossils.

Today paleontologists are joined by pathologists, geologists, biologists, botanists, and scientists from other fields who are much more interested in the biological questions raised by dinosaur and megafauna fossils than in unearthing and cataloging the fossils themselves. Discoveries about social behavior, intelligence, migrations, and extinction are providing a profound new understanding of the process of evolution, which in turn is changing the way we think about all life on Earth, including our own.

(Left) A three-toed sloth lumbers through the Natural History Museum of Los Angeles County.

(Above) An *Allosaurus* could tear great chunks of meat from its victims. Courtesy Dinosaur National Monument.

6
Guide to Museums & Parks

Only the broadest outlines of dinosaur evolutionary relationships are known, and the majority of the relationships inferred for the dinosaur family tree are based on characteristics that can be readily observed and studied in bones. When you visit various museums and dinosaur parks, you will undoubtedly see charts depicting dinosaur ancestry that differ from one another. These differences occur because different paleontologists use different characteristics to classify dinosaurs. And there will be discrepancies (and a

Meanwhile, uncertainty has not prevented paleontologists from attempting to reconstruct dinosaur history with the information that *is* available. Paleontologists know that their stories are as incomplete as the fossil skeletons they uncover, but each new piece of information added to the puzzle provides a more accurate picture of dinosaur life. Be aware that what you see in museums is an *approximation* of what the Mesozoic Period was really like; we'll never know for sure unless time machines are invented to take us back

healthy amount of controversy) about which group of animals gave rise to the dinosaurs and whether modern animals like birds have dinosaurs in their family trees. Much more information needs to be collected before we have definite answers to these questions, but the picture continues to develop as new fossil finds are uncovered and old fossil finds are restudied.

into the past.

One last point to keep in mind when you think about huge meat-eating dinosaurs and fantastic creatures like mammoths and Irish elk is that these creatures represent only a tiny fraction of the diverse animals that lived in the past. Not all dinosaurs were gigantic and terrifying – despite their image in movies and

(Left) Medicine Rock State Park, where teeth and bones of many Paleocene mammals have been found. Courtesy Carter County Museum, Ekalaka, Montana.

T. rex often dined on *Corythosaurus*. Photo by Howard P. Nuerenburger; courtesy Carnegie Museum of Natural History, Pittsburgh, Pennsylvania.

science fiction; many were small, shy insect eaters or peaceful plant munchers. And most of the mammals that lived during the Pleistocene were not giants adorned with magnificent antlers, horns, or tusks. Instead they included numerous small fur-bearing creatures like lemmings, moles, and voles whose evolutionary stories are as fascinating as those of larger mammals. However, public displays in museums are designed to attract attention and to provide an opportunity to learn about certain aspects of prehistoric life. The animals featured are often the biggest or the most exotic looking, but the stories they tell also give us plenty of *general* information about the world of prehistoric animals.

When you plan a visit to one of these sites, you plan an adventure of time and mind; enjoy.

Remember that many museums and parks have changing exhibitions and programs, and some museums are closed on Mondays. Some parks may not allow camping. We recommend that you call before visiting to check times, dates, programs, and facilities.

For lack of information, a number of good museums are not included in this listing. Be sure to check out university, college, and natural history museums in your area. Many of them have dinosaurs or prehistoric mammals on display, often specimens excavated in your own state. Dinosaurs that once roamed your backyard are always the most interesting.

WHERE TO LOOK AND WHAT TO DO IF YOU FIND A FOSSIL

The word *fossil* comes from the Latin for "dug up." Most fossils are embedded in rock formed from sediments such as sand, silt, or mud. Generally fossils are older than 10,000 years, the time of the last ice age. Dinosaur fossils are found in sedimentary rock of Mesozoic origin, 65–248 million years old.

If you go searching for fossils, include plowed fields, old and weathered rock cuts, riverbanks, cliffs and bluffs, coal strip mines, quarries and streambeds, highway cuts through bedrock, gravel, and crushed stones, your own driveway, and any sedimentary rock bed. Even stone walls and foundations, and stone sidewalks in older cities are possibilities.

Good tools to bring along include a hammer, a cold chisel—always chisel *away* from the fossil—a knapsack, box, or basket to carry your fossils, newspaper or tissue to wrap your finds, a pencil and paper to label where you found which specimen, a magnifying glass or hand lens, a camera to record how you found the fossil, and a topographic map to mark where you found them.

Tips:

1. Avoid coarse sediment; it grinds up fossils.
2. *Be sure to secure permission* for digging in quarries and on private property.
3. You will have better luck finding invertebrate fossils because they are more common.
4. Get down on your knees and look CLOSELY at each spot. Take your time.
5. When you use a chisel, cut a narrow trough around the fossil. Once the trough is deeper than the fossil, strike the base of the pillar you have made. The fossil should pop out. If you think you might damage the fossil by using a chisel to remove it, leave it. You can collect it later when the weather has loosened it more.

If you are looking for fossils in state or national parks, remember that the fossils belong to the park and *nothing,* however small, can be removed.

1. Be sure not to disturb anything. After you look at it, put it back the way it was. Don't dig out anything that is buried; you might destroy valuable information.
2. Plot the site of your find on a map, ideally on a 7.5′ USGS Topographical Quad map, but any map will do. Also draw a sketch map of the site.
3. Take as many black and white and color pictures as you can without disturbing your find.
4. Determine who owns the land and let the landowner know about your discovery. Notify appropriate park or paleontologic authorities.

East

Peabody Museum of Natural History
Yale University
170 Whitney Avenue, P.O. Box 6666
New Haven, Connecticut 06511-8161
203-432-3750

Open year round. Admission fee. Call about special programs. The Peabody offers extensive educational programs; call for information.

The largest natural history museum in New England, the Peabody (founded in 1866) is also one of the oldest natural history museums in the country. O.C. Marsh of the Dinosaur Wars was Peabody's nephew and once the museum's curator. On the first floor a huge brontosaur towers above to greet you, with the dinosaurs beneath him — stegosaur, *Triceratops*, camptosaur, and others — dwarfed by his size. Along the walls of the exhibit hall is a beautiful 110-foot labeled mural of the Age of Dinosaurs for which the artist, Rudolph Zallinger, won a Pulitzer Prize. A similar Hall of Mammals features a mastodon and another large mural by Zallinger depicting the animals in their natural habitat. Many of the exhibits here were actually unearthed by Marsh and his team of dinosaur and early mammal hunters.

The parade of dinosaurs at the Peabody Museum of Natural History, Yale University, New Haven, Connecticut.

Dinosaur State Park
West Street
Rocky Hill, Connecticut 06067-3506
203-529-8423

Located a mile east of Interstate 91 (Exit 23). Open year round. Admission fee. Visitors may make casts of dinosaur footprints during the warmer months; call to check.

Large, birdlike *Eubrontes* strode through the sandy mud of the Connecticut River Valley 180 million years ago. These were 8-foot-tall carnivores that splashed through shallow swamps in search of fish or crocodiles to eat. They left behind more than a thousand tracks preserved in stone at Dinosaur State Park.

From May 1 to October 31 families may make one cast of the tracks to take home. Directions are posted, and mixing pails, water, and cast forms are available at the park. Come before 3:30 P.M. and bring:

> 10 pounds of plaster of paris
> ¼ cup of cooking oil
> Paper towels for clean-up
> Rags

There are five tracks available for casting. Following the directions posted at the site, you'll go home with a dinosaur footprint cast weighing about sixteen pounds. It takes forty-five minutes to an hour for the cast to harden, so while you're waiting, you can picnic in the park, walk the nature trails, and soak up more information about dinosaurs.

The Pratt Museum of Natural History
Amherst College
Amherst, Massachusetts 01002
413-542-2165

Open during the academic year and on weekends in the summer. Free admission. Special programs for children.

Edward B. Hitchcock, a New England divine of some repute and for many years the president and a professor of natural history and geology at Amherst College, spent many years collecting and describing Triassic dinosaur footprints in the Connecticut River Valley without ever realizing what they were. Locals dubbed them the footprints of "Noah's ravens, too large to fit in the Ark." From 1835 when he first became interested in the tracks until his death in 1864, Hitchcock believed them to be the tracks of ancient birds. "I have seen, in scientific vision, an apterous [wingless] bird, some twelve or fifteen feet high, — nay, large flocks of them, — walking over the muddy surface, followed by many others of analogous character, but of smaller size." He spent nearly thirty active summers collecting these three-toed tracks for the "Appleton Cabinet," a museum donated to Amherst for the footprint collection.

Today visitors to Amherst's Pratt Museum can visit the extensive dinosaur track collection and gaze upon the prosauropod *Anchisaurus,* an early, 7-foot-long dinosaur that roamed New England in the late Triassic or early Jurassic. As Hitchcock wrote, "Strange, indeed is this menagerie of remote sandstone days."

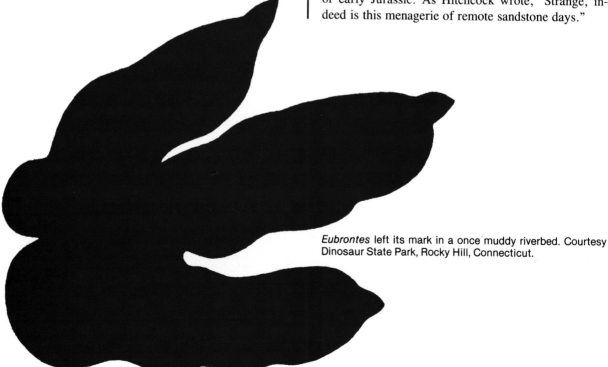

Eubrontes left its mark in a once muddy riverbed. Courtesy Dinosaur State Park, Rocky Hill, Connecticut.

Museum of Science
Science Park
Boston, Massachusetts 02114-1099
617-723-2500

Located off Storrow Drive, accessible by car or the Green Line subway. Open year round. Admission fee.

A hundred million years ago, this toothy grin was part of a living *Tyrannosaurus rex*, the largest carnivorous dinosaur. Courtesy Boston Museum of Science.

The museum hosts many changing exhibits and programs including Dinamation. Call for information.

A life-sized, story-and-a-half tall *T. rex* towers over visitors to the museum; small children aren't even as high as his toe. Smaller models of other dinosaurs roar and roam in the museum, including *Triceratops, Ankylosaurus,* and one of the smallest known dinosaurs, the rooster-sized *Compsognathus* from Europe, which weighed in at about 6 pounds and hunted lizards. There is also a huge ichthyosaur or "fish lizard" fossil. Play dinosaur games or use a Dino Data computer to learn about twenty popular dinosaurs.

The Bergen Museum of Art and Science
Ridgewood Avenue & Farview Avenue
Paramus, New Jersey 07652
201-265-1248

Open year round. Free admission.

Two mastodons that once browsed among the trees in Bergen County (just across the Hudson River from New York City) now make their homes in the Bergen Museum. Junior high school boys unearthed the jawbone of the Hackensack mastodon in 1962. Their find sent Dr. George Whitaker of the American Museum of Natural History on a dig practically in his own backyard. Volunteers recovered mastodon rib bones, vertebrae, tusks, and jaws as well as the remains of fourteen other prehistoric animals. The Hackensack mastodon bones are displayed in the Bergen Museum as they appeared in the process of excavation.

The Dwarskill mastodon turned up during excavations for the Hackensack Water Company. Volunteers under the direction of the American Museum of Natural History recovered 200 bones, scrubbed them clean, shellacked, and repaired them. Three amateur paleontologists rebuilt the bones into a skeleton using drawings and sketches as a guide and replacing missing parts with casts. The finished skeleton measures 24 feet and weighs 900 pounds.

It's hard to believe that mammoths once wandered the wetlands of New Jersey. Courtesy Bergen Museum of Art and Science.

Buffalo Museum of Science
1020 Humboldt Parkway
Buffalo, New York 14211-1293
716-896-5200

Open year round. Admission fee. Call for special programs.

The Buffalo Museum of Science has a permanent hall dedicated to dinosaurs and called "Dinosaurs & Co." This exhibit includes fossils, casts, and illustrations of animals and plants from the Age of Dinosaurs. Dinosaur teeth, dinosaur eggs, gizzard stones, impressions of dinosaur skin, and dinosaur footprints accompany an *Allosaurus,* a *Triceratops,* and psittacosaurs (2- to 6-foot plant-eating dinosaurs with parrotlike beaks), as well as casts and parts of many other dinosaurs and fossils from earlier and later periods. *Dinosaurs: Fifteen Questions and Answers,* available for $.50 from the museum, gives clear, up-to-date answers to some common dinosaur questions.

American Museum of Natural History
Central Park West at 79th Street
New York, New York 10024-5192
212-769-5100

Open all year. Admission fee. Call for special programs. Accessible by car, bus, or the IND subway line.

The American Museum of Natural History (AMNH) sponsored Roy Chapman Andrews's legendary dinosaur hunt in the Gobi Desert in the 1920s which inspired the Indiana Jones movies. At this writing, AMNH is in the process of creating a new home for its world-renowned dinosaur collection — the largest in the United States — as well as the mammoths, saber-toothed cats, and other fossil vertebrates residing there. It houses one of the world's two dinosaur mummy fossils and more than 260,000 fossil vertebrates, the largest collection in the world. The entire fourth floor is being reconfigured into six new halls that will tell the story of the evolution of vertebrate life with fossils, models, displays, murals, and interactive computer terminals.

The first creature in this massive project is the spectacular new *Barosaurus.* Currently on view in Theodore Roosevelt Memorial Hall, this exhibit depicts a dramatic scene that could have happened 140 million years ago — a female *Barosaurus* rearing up fifty feet in the air to protect her young from a hungry *Allosaurus*

on the prowl. The incredibly long-necked barosaurs munched conifers in South Dakota and Wyoming in the late Jurassic.

You can watch the work in progress until its completion (scheduled for December, 1995) and enjoy many changing, temporary exhibits until then. New specimens will come out of the closet, and old favorites like *Tyrannosaurus rex* will return in dramatic new poses. You could spend a week here!

T. rex. Aren't you glad they're extinct? Photo by Harvey A. Duze; courtesy The Academy of Natural Sciences of Philadelphia (described on page 54).

(Left) Dinosaur going up! Workers erect the spectacular *Barosaurus* exhibit at the American Museum of Natural History.

This *Dapedoglossis testis* from the Green River Shale of Wyoming was a powerful swimmer 40 million years ago. Courtesy Carter County Museum, Ekalaka, Montana.

Petrified Creatures Museum of Natural History
RD #2, Route 20
Richfield Springs, New York 13439
315-858-2868

Located on U.S. Route 20, eleven miles north of the Baseball Hall of Fame in Cooperstown. Open May 15 to October 15. Admission fee.

This privately run museum located on the site of an ancient coral reef is a special treat for small children because they can dig here for fossils that they can take home. The staff gives digging demonstrations and no one goes home without a fossil. There are also brightly colored outdoor dinosaurs that can be climbed and are just waiting for their portraits to be snapped with young visitors. Be sure to explore the museum itself (built right in the rocks), featuring fossils from the Devonian period, the Age of Fishes. Because of the geologic stability of the area, the fossils in the rock strata here are layered in order of age. The ages of Devonian fossils throughout the world are measured against the "index fossils" found in Central New York, including the collection at this museum.

The Academy of Natural Sciences of Philadelphia
Nineteenth & Ben Franklin Parkway
Philadelphia, Pennsylvania 19103-1195
215-299-1000

Open all year. Admission fee. Call for special programs.

The "Discovering Dinosaurs" exhibit combines an excellent display of dinosaur and other Mesozoic reptile skeletons, including a *T. Rex* cast, with a variety of interactive exhibits where you can have fun learning about dinosaurs.

In 1856 Dr. Joseph Leidy of the Academy published the first description of dinosaur remains from North America—fossil teeth from the Judith River in Montana. In 1858, this museum became the first in the world to display a mounted dinosaur skeleton when Leidy and a sculptor named Waterhouse Hawkins assembled and reconstructed parts of a nearly complete hadrosaur discovered in nearby New Jersey. Leidy was the first to determine that dinosaurs could be bipedal. Writing in 1858, he said, "The great disproportion of size between the fore and back parts of the skeleton of *Hadrosaurus* leads me to suspect that this great extinct herbivorous lizard may have been in the habit of browsing, sustaining itself, kangaroo-like, in an erect

position on its back extremities and tail."

The Academy was also home base for Edward Drinker Cope, O.C. Marsh's arch rival in the Dinosaur Wars, and has in its collection numerous fossils he discovered or identified as well as a Delaware Valley dinosaur collection and many other specimens.

The Carnegie Museum of Natural History
4400 Forbes Avenue
Pittsburgh, Pennsylvania 15213-4080
412-622-3243

Located in the Oakland section of Pittsburgh. Open year round. Admission fee. Call for special programs.

Known as the Home of the Dinosaurs, the Carnegie enjoys the third largest dinosaur collection in the United States. Every Saturday and Sunday you can take a free guided tour of the Dinosaur Hall, where you walk around and under the huge skeletons of eleven different species and examine about 500 fossil specimens. *Diplodocus carnegii,* the first dinosaur discovered by the museum, stretches all 84 feet of its length across

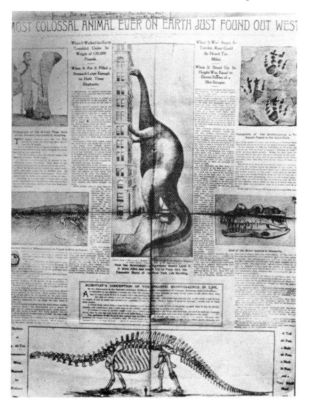

"The Most Colossal Animal on Earth Just Found Out West." *New York Journal,* November 1889. Acquisition of this skeleton marked the beginning of the Carnegie dinosaur collection.

(Right) Denizens of long ago march through Dinosaur Hall at the Carnegie Museum of Natural History.

the Hall, and one of the few actual *T. rex* skeletons ever found bares its terrible teeth. Most of the dinosaur specimens in the Carnegie come from the Morrison Formation in Utah where the environment preserved some of the best big dinosaurs in the world.

A full-page spread in the *New York Journal* of November 1889 exclaimed, "Most Colossal Animal Ever on Earth Just Found Out West!" The *Journal* article featured a sketch of the dinosaur on its hind legs peeking into the eleventh floor of the New York Life Building, a picture of a mustachioed human dwarfed by a *Brontosaurus* thigh bone, and a drawing of the fully articulated skeleton with a human coming half-way up its knee. Full of superlatives – "When it ate it filled a stomach large enough to hold three elephants" – the article credited a team led by William Reed and O.C. Marsh with discovering the dinosaur in the famous quarry at Como Bluff, Wyoming. From his New York City mansion, with only the *Journal* raves to go by, millionaire philanthropist Andrew Carnegie cabled the curator of his Pittsburgh Museum: "Dear Chancellor, Buy this for Pittsburgh" – and enclosed a $10,000 check.

The transition from 86 feet of solid rock in Wyoming to the dramatic skeleton in Pittsburgh involved eight years of arduous work, but the huge *Diplodocus carnegii* skeleton eventually joined the *Brontosaurus* already in the museum. Carnegie went into dinosaur collecting in a big way and funded major expeditions in the American West. A royal hint from King Edward VII that the British Museum might like to obtain such a specimen resulted in Carnegie's donating exact copies of his *Diplodocus* to museums in nine capitals around

the world. Until his death in 1919, Carnegie was personally interested in the program of fossil gathering and contributed generously to it. In recognition of his support, an earlier find of O.C. Marsh was renamed *Apatosaurus louisa* after Mrs. Carnegie.*

The *Apatosaurus louisa* skeleton at the Carnegie Museum is 76½ feet long from tail to nose. Its huge three-clawed feet measure 26 inches across. Chipping the *Apatosaurus* out of the rock at what is now Dinosaur National Monument in Utah took many months, and four horse teams were needed to haul the crated bones to the nearest railhead. No skull was found with the original skeleton, and it was not until 1979 – seventy years after its discovery – that the appropriate (though incongruously tiny) head was fitted in place. This tiny head has enough room for only a bare-bones brain and a set of rather inconsequential teeth (which were supplemented by gizzard stones like those in a modern grain-eating bird).

Both *Diplodocus* and *Apatosaurus* were sauropods, the largest terrestrial animals ever. A massive, cleverly engineered arch of vertebrae with many hollow bones, and sturdy tree-trunk legs provided the support system for these animals that weighed in at 30–35 *tons*. Because of their great weight, there has been some debate over whether an adult could move about on land. Certainly there is fossil evidence that they were swamp dwellers, and some paleontologists banished them to a half-submerged life to allow water to support some of their weight. But Roland Bird's discovery of sauropod tracks in Glen Rose, Texas, put that idea to rest. Sauropods could walk – not run, but walk – on land, sometimes dragging their tails behind them.

Getting a closer look at the Carnegie.

* It was later discovered that *Apatosaurus* and *Brontosaurus* were the same animal. The first assigned name takes precedence, so although most people know this dinosaur as *Brontosaurus* the "thunder lizard," its correct name is *Apatosaurus*.

Parc de Miguasha
C.P. 183
Nouvelle, Quebec, Canada G0C 2E0
418-794-2475

Located on the Gaspé Peninsula at Chaleur Bay. Take the ferry across the St. Lawrence River from Dalhousie, New Brunswick. Open May 15 to September 30. Guided tours in both English and French.

En Gaspésie, au bord de la rivière Ristigouche, tout au fond de la baie des Chaleurs, une petite localité du nom de Migausha abrite l'un des plus prestigieux sites fossilifères. Les fossiles découverts à ce jour ont permis à la paléontolgie de poser des jalons importants dans la recherche des origines des espèces animales et l'invasion de la terre par les poissons. La découverte ici des anciens poissons sans mâchoires, des poisson avec peau faite de plaques osseuses, des poissons à épines, des poissons osseux, des poissons ayant deux systèmes respiratoires et des poissons ayant des nageoires en forme de frange explique l'importance donnée au site par les paléontologues du monde entier. Comme aucune de celles-ci n'a survécu jusqu'à nos jours, le paléontologue se voit forcé d'en décrire l'anatomie à partir des marques incrustées dans la pierre. Par des études comparatives avec la faune aquatique actuelle, il tente ainsi de reconstituer l'écologie et le comportement des groupes disparus.

In the cliffs of Miguasha on the Baie des Chaleurs is a fossil record that traces the first vertebrate steps on dry land. It is the only place in the world where you can follow the evolution of aquatic vertebrates (fish) to terrestrial vertebrates (tetrapods) in the layers of sandstone. Fossil fish from water dwellers to puddle-jumping land dwellers with lungs have been unearthed here. One of the most interesting museum presentations in North America, Parc de Miguasha includes an outstanding interpretation center, a teaching laboratory, and cliffs where visitors are encouraged to participate in research and try their luck at discovering a fossil specimen.

The Devonian era began 400 million years ago. As continents began to rise and dry out, the climate swung between torrential rains and droughts. Swamps turned into mountains; the Appalachians rose to stretch 2,000 miles from Newfoundland to Alabama. Dragonflies, ferns, conifers, and the first forests spread across the drying land, but the only vertebrates remained behind in the receding waters. The Parc de Miguasha collection includes fierce predatory ancestors of true fish that terrorized the inhabitants of ancient Lac de Miguasha. As the lake receded, fish were trapped flopping and dying in the dwindling pools where rotting vegetation robbed the water of oxygen. Lungfish, with their two breathing systems — both lungs and gills — could stick

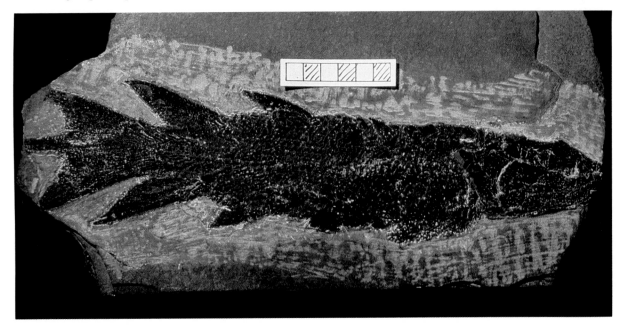

Eusthenopteron was a pioneer whose lungs, strong vertebrae and sturdy fins made possible the first vertebrate forays onto dry land. Photo by Fred Klus; courtesy Parc de Miguasha.

their heads above the stagnant water to snatch a gulp of air and survive in drying puddles. Gradually, *Eusthenopteron* evolved with not only strong lungs, but with strong vertebrae for support on land, and the skeletal patterns of legs in its four sturdy fins that allowed it to scramble briefly across the mud in search of more water in a larger puddle.

More amphibious creatures developed that moved on land with a bellydragging, wiggling motion that put little strain on their legs. These were pioneers, the beginning of land vertebrates. Because amphibians must lay their unprotected eggs in ponds with little food to sustain the embryos, even the most terrestrial were still tied to water. The changing, drying world placed a premium on vertebrates that did not depend on ponds and streams that were likely to dry up. Ferny forests inhabited only by invertebrates beckoned with new food and better habitats. Natural selection favored better legs and better eggs: reptiles.

National Museum of Natural History
Smithsonian Institution
10th Street & Constitution Avenue, N.W.
Washington, D.C. 20560
202-357-1300

Open year round. Call for special programs.

The second largest dinosaur collection in the United States is well worth a visit. Plan to spend at least an afternoon in Dinosaur Hall, where skeletons of *Albertosaurus, Tyrannosaurus rex, Maiasaura, Stegosaurus, Triceratops*, and models of other well-known dinosaurs loom large around you. Trace a lighted time line and climb on Mr. Beasely, a life-sized *Triceratops*.

Check out the Ice Age Mammals exhibit, especially the incredible Irish elk with its 10-foot antler span, the evolving horses, and the denizens of the tar pit. You can run your fingers over mammoth and mastodon teeth to compare these Pleistocene giants, or you can watch a colorful slide program on glaciation.

The fossil menagerie includes a toothy *Dinichthys*, 12-foot terror of Devonian seas, the elegant calligraphy of crinoid (or sea lily) fossils, a double fossil of one fish swallowed inside the other, and the truly ancient Australian fossil algae from 3.5 billion years ago.

South

Florida Museum of Natural History
University of Florida
Gainesville, Florida 32611
904-392-1721

Open year round. Free admission. Special programs.

During the various ice ages, Florida remained green and warm. Animals pushed south by glaciers found food and refuge there. An example is the Florida cave bear, about four times the size of its living cousin the Andean spectacled bear, which roamed among the riverbanks and sinkholes of the south. Heavy-limbed and stocky, its teeth proclaim the bear a vegetarian. Because advancing and retreating glaciers did not grind up or disturb their fossil remains, Florida has an unusually rich fossil legacy, especially of mammals.

Georgia Southern Museum
Landrum Box 801
Statesboro, Georgia 30460-8061
912-681-5444

Open year round. Call for special programs.

Ferocious, meat-eating mosasaurs once ruled the seas that covered much of southern Georgia while *T. rex* reigned with terror on the land up north. Twenty-six feet long and equipped with gaping jaws and sixteen to eighteen continuously-replaced sharp teeth, the mosasaur could swallow just about anything it could catch. The Georgia Southern Museum's mosasaur fossil, one of the most complete in the world, today swims in place with its broad flat tail, bony plated head, and wide paddles. Visitors can also see a video of the paleontologists recovering the fossil and learn how fossil casts and molds are made for display.

Big Bone Lick State Park
3380 Beaver Road
Union, Kentucky 41091-9627
606-384-3522

Located 22 miles southwest of Covington. Open year round. Camping, fishing, hiking. Admission fee.

In prehistoric times great herds of giant mastodons, mammoths, bison, primitive horses, stag moose, and sloths browsed in this area of north central Kentucky. Driven southward by the Ice Age and attracted by the salt found in abundance in the swamp, the huge beasts mired down in the ooze and died. When Indians guided French explorer Charles Le Moyne to Big Bone Lick in 1739, bones lay in profusion on the marshy ground. Several huge bones were packed up and sent back as curiosities to the French king. A later explorer packed off tusks and teeth to Ben Franklin, who found them "extremely curious on many accounts." Thomas Jefferson instructed William Clark of Lewis and Clark fame to collect bones for him at Big Bone Lick, probably the first organized paleontological expedition in the United States. The bones of hundreds of mammals have been removed from the area. Today you can visit the warm salt springs and see some of the bones and research material displayed in the museum along with life-sized models, a model dig, and a live herd of buffaloes.

North Carolina Museum of Life and Science
433 Murray Avenue
Durham, North Carolina 27704
919-220-5429

Open year round. Admission fee. Call for special programs.

Sauropod bones and dinosaur reconstructions at a busy museum with a lot of child appeal.

Texas Memorial Museum
2400 Trinity
Austin, Texas 78705
512-471-1604

Open year round. Free admission. Call for special programs.

Affiliated with the University of Texas, this museum has a stong vertebrate paleontology program with a laboratory, a radiocarbon dating facility, and an especially good Mesozoic fossil collection.

An image of dinosaurs that once fought and browsed in Texas. Courtesy Dinosaur Valley State Park.

Panhandle-Plains Historical Museum
2401 Fourth Avenue
Canyon, Texas 79015
806-656-2244

Open year round. Free admission. Call for special programs.

Check out the collection of local Triassic reptiles that are older than the dinosaurs.

An early drawing of *Triceratops*.

Dinosaur Valley State Park
Box 396
Glen Rose, Texas 76043
817-897-4588

Located in central Texas. Open year round. Camping available.

There is no branch of detective science which is so important and so much neglected as the art of tracing footsteps. — Arthur Conan Doyle, 1891

Three kinds of dinosaur tracks make fascinating detective work at Dinosaur Valley State Park, which also features 1,500 acres of wildlife, hiking, and river wading. Sauropod tracks followed by carnivorous *T. rex* ancestor tracks are located here, as well as the tracks of a smaller, two-legged, birdlike dinosaur. The tracks are often under water in the Paluxy River so check on river conditions if you plan to visit. The visitor center houses additional tracks, murals, bones, and two huge dinosaur models donated by Sinclair.

In the 1940s, Roland Bird (who worked for many years with Barnum Brown of the American Museum of Natural History) came across some fossilized footprints for sale in a rock shop and decided to track down their source. Poking around near Glen Rose, Texas, he realized that the odd potholes running under some rubble were dinosaur tracks; he was "standing in the right rear footprint of a brontosaur-like creature." Bird's discovery and analysis of dinosaur footprints not only took the brontosaur out of the water and set him firmly on land but also introduced some ideas about dinosaur herd behavior and socialization.

The sedimentary rock in Texas speaks of a time 140 million years ago when a group of nine dinosaurs slogged through sandy mud in the aftermath of a storm that had swept the beaches clear. Forty feet long, with a 10-foot stride and a 54-inch footprint, these huge, slow sauropods apparently scented danger from a predator and turned toward the sea to escape. Bird and his WPA workers uncovered bipedal predator tracks swiftly pursuing the herd and were able to follow the drama until it disappeared in the rubble of geologic upheavals. We'll never know if the peaceful brontosaurs made it safely to the sea.

Although each individual dinosaur had only one

skeleton to give for the fossil record, each left millions of footprints. Thousands of fossilized dinosaur trackways have been uncovered all over the world. Not only can they tell us about size, weight, speed, and stride, but they also tell us something about socialization; for example, Bird proved that dinosaurs traveled in herds, something modern reptiles never do. Subsequent footprint discoveries suggest dinosaur herds may have included mothers surrounding babies in the protection of a herd; motherly devotion is also not a common trait of modern reptiles. The herd idea is reinforced by the dinosaur tracks at Dinosaur State Park in Connecticut and the Peace River in British Columbia. Light tracks elsewhere in Texas provide evidence of a floating brontosaur pushing off with his hind leg to swim, so we know they spent some time in the water. Other tracks show the marks of a dragged tail, another indication that brontosaurs could walk on land.

Paleoichnologists—students of fossil footprints—need at least three footprints in order to determine stride, pace, and walking efficiency. Dinosaurs did not always leave the same footprints: they only sometimes appeared clawed or lobed depending on how fast the animal was moving. Footprints have to be made in exactly the right conditions to become fossilized, and these conditions do not favor bone fossilization. Therefore, the skeletal remains of the footprint makers are not usually found near the footprints. This makes it very difficult to determine exactly which dinosaur made which footprint. However, careful study of footprints has helped elevate the dinosaur's image from a saurian sprawler to the upright, efficient-walking, straight-legs-under-the-body dinosaurs you see in modern museums.

Houston Museum of Natural Science
1 Hermann Circle Drive
Houston, Texas 77030
713-639-4600

Located south of downtown in Hermann Park next to the Texas Medical Center. Admission fee. Features a number of changing prehistoric programs; celebrates its excellent dinosaur skeleton and cast collection with an annual "Dinosaur Dash" for costumed kids and serious running adults. Call for information.

Imagine a flying reptile with wings larger than the 38-foot 5-inch wingspan of an F-4 fighter jet, swooping across the skies of West Texas in search of food. *Quetzalcoatlus northropi* ruled the skies some 64 million years ago, and Houston has the largest specimen ever found to date: the fossil remains of this lofty reptile suggest a wingspan of nearly 50 feet!

The first flying reptile was found in Jurassic limestone along with jellyfish and was classified as a sea creature. It was not until Cuvier got a good look at it in 1809 that it was recognized for what it was, a flying reptile. Cuvier named it *Pterodactyl,* "wing finger," because the wing skin was stretched over a hollow framework of arm bones.

It took drastic evolutionary remodeling of a terrestrial ancestor to produce the *Pterodactyl.* Early publications described it as a flying dragon; probably it was the consummate gliding aerialist. O.C. Marsh found specimens in Kansas with wingspans of 22 to 27 feet. But it was in Texas (where else?) that a lucky graduate student unearthed the *Quetzalcoatlus,* the biggest *Pterodactyl* ever.

Engineers are skeptical that such a huge creature could actually fly or even take off, but it is difficult to do meaningful engineering feasibility studies on an animal that lived over 64 million years ago. The tubular strut design of the *Pterodactyl*'s hollow bones included a sternum (breastbone) to anchor flight muscles, but whether these flight muscles were strong enough to flap such huge wings is uncertain. However, engineers and paleontologists have been able to build an accurate half-size remote-controlled model of the dinosaur that has flown successfully for television and film.

Pterodactyls ranged from sparrow size up. If they were limited to soaring and gliding, these sight-hunting

The awesome wing of *Quetzalcoatlus*. Courtesy Houston
Museum of Natural Science.

fishermen may have had difficulty taking off from water or ground and might have had to use the hooklike claws on their wings to pull themselves up into trees or convenient cliffs for takeoff. On the other hand, it is difficult to attribute their apparent success – *Pterodactyls* have turned up on several continents – with this kind of precarious life-style. It was not until the discovery of small feathered *Archaeopteryx* that flapping flight is a certainty.

Other Texas-sized exhibits at the Houston museum include a huge *Diplodocus* skeleton that recently received a pedicure to replace its fiberglass toes with actual *Diplodocus* toe bones. In the Ice Age collection, a giant six-foot armadillo skeleton and its sculptured look-alike join saber-toothed cats and early three-toed horses the size of collies.

This giant armadillo looks for a meal beneath a log at the Houston Museum of Natural Science.

Midwest

Field Museum of Natural History
Lake Shore Drive at Roosevelt Road
Chicago, Illinois 60605
312-922-9410

Open year round. Admission fee. Call for special programs.

For the first time in a very long time the dinosaurs — at least the six whose skeletons live at the Field — are on the move again to get ready for a permanent new exhibit on evolution called "Life Over Time." The dinosaurs debut in 1993, the mammals in 1994, and an exhibit on plate tectonics, volcanoes, and earthquakes is scheduled for later opening. (Plate tectonics is the study of the shifting plates that cover the surface of the earth. Their movement causes mountains to rise and fall, climates to change, continents to drift, and earthquakes and volcanoes to rumble.) Although the *Albertosaurus* no longer towers above its *Lambeosaurus* lunch during the renovations, there are many ongoing exhibits and interesting works in progress. The Field houses a fine collection of more than thirty-four fossil dinosaurs and reptiles, plus mastodons, mammoths, saber-toothed cats, and other Pleistocene mammals.

Fryxell Geology Museum
Augustana College
Rock Island, Illinois 61201
309-794-7318

Just off 38th Street, two blocks north of 7th Avenue. Open year round.

This little museum is specially tuned to teach children about fossils. It offers many examples, programs and tours, guides for teachers and families, and hands-on experiences. The collection is not extensive but includes casts of a *T. rex* skull and a *Triceratops,* and a wealth of fossils. There is a planetarium nearby on the campus.

(Right) An *Albertosaurus* lunching on a *Lambeosaurus*. Courtesy Field Museum of Natural History.

(Pages 66-67) In the Hall of Paleontology. Photo by Jeffrey P. Grosscup. Courtesy Science Museum of Minnesota (described on page 69).

Kansas University Museum of Natural History
University of Kansas
Dyche Hall
Lawrence, Kansas 66045-2454
913-864-4540

Open year round. Donations are suggested. Many special programs.

More than a million natural history specimens, primarily from the Great Plains, await your visit. Special programs are available for children and adults.

The University of Michigan Exhibit Museum
1109 Geddes Ave
Ann Arbor, Michigan 48109-1079
313-764-0478

Open year round. Admission fee for groups. Call for special programs.

Fossils, dinosaurs, and well-known megafauna such as smilodont, mastodon, and extinct rhinoceros stalk the halls at the University Museum and get involved in many special programs.

Browsing among the fossils. Photo by Jeffrey P. Grosscup; courtesy of the Science Museum of Minnesota.

The Michigan State University Museum
West Circle Drive
East Lansing, Michigan 48824
517-355-2370

Open year round. Free admission. Call for special programs.

Features a big walk-through Hall of Life with fossils and murals of Mesozoic reptile stars.

Great Lakes Area Paleontological Museum
381 South Long Lake Road
Traverse City, Michigan 49684
616-943-8850

Open daily by arrangement with the curator. Free admission.

Displays more than 15 million specimens, including all phyla of fossils found in the Grand Traverse area, plus fossil fish from two inches to six feet in length and from early evolution models to lungfish.

Science Museum of Minnesota
30 East Tenth Street
St. Paul, Minnesota 55101
612-221-9488

Open year round. Admission fee. Call for special programs.

Visitors can walk around and under the 82-foot-long *Diplodocus,* the *Allosaurus,* and the *Camptosaurus* in the newly renovated dinosaur hall. Discovered by a retired Minnesota teacher and his students in Wyoming who called in the museum when they realized they were onto something big, the huge *Diplodocus* skeleton was field-jacketed in plaster and removed to the Science Museum. The public was able to watch the assembly of the two-story skeleton during the 1991 "Dinosaurs Going Up" exhibition. The dinosaur laboratory window is always open so you can watch paleontology in progress. Other exhibits explain how scientists excavate fossils, and include prehistoric rhinoceros and crocodile fossils from the Midwest.

The *Diplodocus* is a classic dinosaur shape with a long neck and tail. Although about the length of a tennis court, *Diplodocus* was not exactly on the ball; it spent most of its time drowsing in swampy areas of what are now the Rocky Mountain states, relying on its incredible size and whiplash tail for defense rather than on speed or brainpower. Despite its colossal size, its slim limbs and lightened skeleton meant it only tipped the scales at a gossamer 11.7 tons.

Agate Fossil Beds National Monument
Scotts Bluff National Monument
Box 427
Gering, Nebraska 69341

Located in northwest Nebraska. Write the Superintendent for more information.

The visitor center has exhibits on the fossil story with a nearby self-guiding trail to exposed fossils. In the works are plans to expose additional fossil remains and build interpretive structures and more extensive display buildings.

Agate Fossil Beds has concentrations of mammal fossils in sedimentary rock formed about 19 million

Haplocanthosaurus delfsi strrrretches over the Cleveland Museum of Natural History exhibits.

(Pages 70-71) *Nanotyrannus.* Courtesy Cleveland Museum of Natural History.

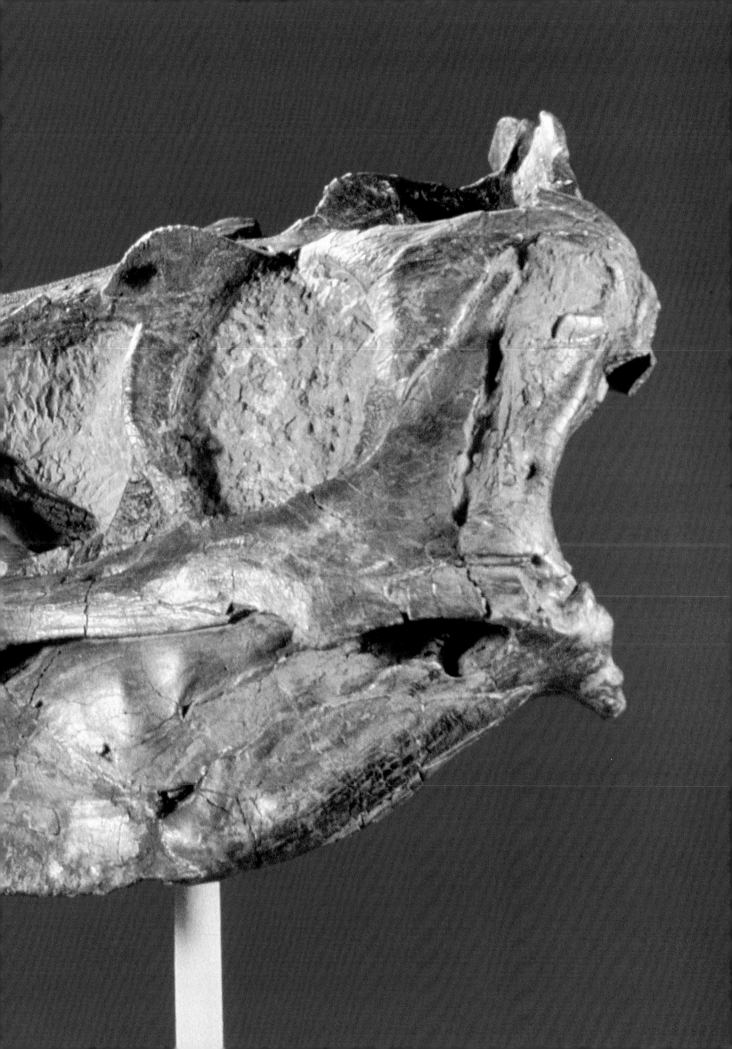

years ago. Long a favorite fossil site for early paleontologists from Yale, Amherst, the University of Nebraska, the Carnegie Museum, and the American Museum of Natural History, bones from the site have been exhibited throughout the world. Two-horned rhinoceroses the size of Shetland ponies, the cumbersome *Moropus* with the front legs of a rhino and back legs like a bear, the ferocious, seven-foot "Terrible Pig" (*Dinohyus*), and the graceful little *Stenomylus* once roamed these plains.

University of Nebraska State Museum

307 Morrill Hall
14th and U Streets
Lincoln, Nebraska 68588-0338
402-472-3779

Open year round. Free admission. Call for special programs.

More than ten million natural history specimens, primarily from the Central Plains, are housed in this museum collection. Included are both vertebrate and invertebrate fossils.

Cincinnati Museum of Natural History

1301 Western Avenue
Cincinnati, Ohio 45203
513-287-7020

Located in the Museum Center in the restored Union Terminal. Open year round. Admission fee. Call for special programs.

A wonderful new exhibit opened in 1991. Walk into the ice-blue heart of a glacier and into a spring day 19,000 years ago. Meltwater gushes over the sides of the glacier's icy face into ponds and bogs below. Feel the damp wind on your face. Listen to the glacial creaks and groans and the roar of huge Ice Age mammals. Fossils of giant ground sloths, peccaries, and elk-moose; computers and interactive games; sculptures and aroma, lighting, and sound effects — all combine to make this the most realistic possible trip to the Ice Age.

Cleveland Museum of Natural History

Wade Oval, University Circle
Cleveland, Ohio 44106-1767
216-231-4600

Open year round. Admission fee. Call for special programs.

For amateurs interested in fossils, Cleveland sponsors a Fossil Society with workshops, field trips, and activities, and special educational and live-animal programs. Children and families are welcome.

Step into the Hall of Earth Sciences where dramatic displays demonstrate the shifting physical forces at work in our restless globe. View the effects of earthquakes, volcanoes, and erosion on the earth's surface. Discover prehistoric creatures that once roamed the world. See fossil remains of plants and huge dinosaurs such as *Stegosaurus*, *Nanotyrannus*, and *Haplocanthosaurus*. Several of these are unique to the Cleveland Museum.

Nanotyrannus is like a *Tyrannosaurus rex* in a pygmy size: 17 feet long, 1000 pounds. This enfant terrible was built for speed and had a powerful neck and jaws, wicked teeth, and binocular vision just like his larger carnivorous relative, but his skull seems to indicate even more sophisticated senses of hearing, eyesight, and smell that bear a striking resemblance to today's birds. The *Haplocanthosaurus* at the Cleveland is a particularly good specimen of this long-necked herbivore — measuring 72 feet from stem to stern — from the late Jurassic Period.

A giant elk, a saber-toothed cat, and an American mastodon stand as reminders of the Ice Age, and you can trace the origins of mankind and meet "Lucy," the oldest, most complete fossil skeleton of a human ancestor.

The toothy grin of *Haplocanthosaurus delfsi* at the Cleveland Museum of Natural History.

Volunteers number mammoth bones at The Mammoth Site of
Hot Springs. Photo by Brian Cluer.

Royal Ontario Museum

100 Queen's Park
Toronto, Ontario, Canada M5S 2C6
416-586-5549

Open year round. Admission fee. Call for special programs.

More than thirteen dinosaur specimens stalk the Dinosaur Halls of the Royal Ontario, including albertosaurs, stegosaurs, and allosaurs. *Albertosaurus* is a dinosaur first discovered by Joseph Tyrrell in the valley of the Red Deer River in central Alberta, the site of the present-day Royal Tyrrell Museum. Carried out of the canyon where it was found by packhorse and then buckboard across the badlands, its discoverers anxiously protecting it from the jarring ride, the albertosaur skull traveled east to the Canadian capital where is was prepared and preserved. Such a magnificent carnivore (like a smaller, lighter *T. rex*) stimulated great interest in excavating dinosaurs in Alberta and began a dinosaur rush there in the late 1880s. Allosaurs, the tigers of their times, were flesh eaters as large as a bus that may have hunted in packs. Their great gaping jaws and curved teeth meant they could swallow large chunks of meat from the huge lumbering dinosaurs that were their prey.

The Mammoth Site of Hot Springs

Box 606
Hot Springs, South Dakota 57747
605-745-6017

Open year round. Admission fee.

At the Mammoth Site of Hot Springs, under a huge vaulted building, an entire sinkhole of mammoth fossils is preserved in situ. Layer after layer of terraced rock reveal these huge elephant ancestors. The bones of more than 100 mammoths — both wooly and Columbian — along with a great short-faced bear, extinct pronghorn, camel, and peccary have been found. You can watch the laborious process of recovery: removing sediment with trowel and brush, coating the bones with resin, adding a plaster jacket, and carefully chipping from the surrounding rock. The Mammoth Site also has an assembled mammoth skeleton, scale models depicting mammoth evolution, life-sized sil-houettes of twenty-five animals found at the site, a huge aquarium, and a bison-kill exhibit. Self-guiding brochures are available in a variety of languages. Many hands-on experiences allow you to participate in screening for fossils, skeletal assembly, calculating mammoth age by teeth, and identifying fossil finds.

In 1519, according to Bernal Diaz, chronicler of the Cortez expedition to Mexico, a tribe of Aztecs presented Cortez and his men with a huge bone to indicate that theirs was a land of giants. The bone was shipped with due ceremony back to Spain. It is hard to imagine losing a six-foot bone, but King Charles I of Spain's mind was focused entirely on Mexican gold, and the bone disappeared in some castle housecleaning. Probably the bone presented to Cortez was the thighbone of a mastodon from the river valleys of Tlascala.

Ancestors of mammoths and mastodons crossed the Beringa land bridge to Alaska millions of years ago to populate North America and some of South America with elephant ancestors. Mastodons browsed among leaves and vegetation in the swamps of the eastern United States. Shorter and stockier than mammoths, their foreheads were sloped and their teeth suitable for eating leaves, not grass.

Literally thousands of mammoth and mastodon bones have been recovered. Because they are large, abundant, and near the ground surface, people are likely to find the bones, and they certainly attract attention. Mammoth and mastodon skeletons were the first fossils to receive truly scientific consideration by noted scientists such as Georges Cuvier. The science of vertebrate paleontology was established with the study of these huge animals.

Mammoth foot, pedicure complete. Rushmore Photo.
Courtesy of The Mammoth Site of Hot Springs.

During the French and Indian Wars, Charles Le Moyne sent bones to France (probably from Big Bone Lick in what is now Kentucky) which Cuvier named *le grand mostodonte de l'Ohio*. Mastodons captured the imagination of Americans, too: George Washington had a tooth; Franklin and Jefferson speculated about them. Despite the obvious evidence of their teeth, for a while they were branded as fearsome carnivores.

Ironically, it was not the scholars and scientists who first correctly identified mammoths in the early eighteenth century — they rambled on about monsters — but African slaves in California recognized elephant teeth when they saw them. Mammoths were real elephants with long legs, domed heads, massive sequential cheek teeth serrated like a washboard for eating grass, and great curving tusks which in old bulls sometimes crossed and turned back toward the body. An imperator mammoth was found at La Brea which measures 13 feet, 6 inches at the shoulder. Mammoths lived in the Southwest; a shaggier relative with a 2-inch dense, dark undercoat and 20-inch-long outer hair lived in Alaska, where whole frozen mammoths have been unearthed.

Badlands National Park

P.O. Box 6
Interior, South Dakota 57750
605-433-5361

Open all year. Camping available.

Badlands National Park is famous for its fantastically eroded landscapes. Fossils 37 to 23 million years old from the Age of Mammals emerge from eroding buttes and gullies while modern pronghorns, bison, and bighorn sheep drift across old homesteads and the prairie hunting grounds of the Sioux Indians. Along the Fossil Exhibit Trail, you'll view fossils in situ and see casts of common park fossils that tell of the transition to prairie mammals. There is also a Touch Room where you can meet some of the Badlands' oldest residents up close and personal.

Milwaukee Public Museum

800 West Wells Street
Milwaukee, Wisconsin 53233
414-278-2702

Located in downtown Milwaukee near the Civic Center. Open all year. Admission fee. Call for special programs.

Milwaukee is home of the *Torosaurus*, a *Triceratops* relative with a frilled, horned skull the size of a Volkswagen, which was unearthed in the museum's Dig-a-Dinosaur expedition to Montana in 1981. This formidable "bull lizard" dined on tough-leaved plants in the western United States. The many scars on his frill suggest he was quick to pick a fight. At twice the length of a rhinoceros and with the weight of a big bull elephant, he must have been a match for his meat-eating enemies.

The Third Planet exhibit takes you on a trip through time in the Midwest that includes a prehistoric tropical reef, a limestone cave, coal swamps, a *Stegosaurus*, a life-sized diorama of *T. rex* lunching on *Triceratops*, and a walk through a glacier with a gathering of Ice Age stars like the mastodon and saber-toothed cat. Fossils of many of the animals shown in the models, paintings, and videos accompany the displays. Milwaukee has a very active paleontology department with special programs, expeditions, and tours.

A Silurian reef exhibit shows how different Wisconsin was 400 million years ago. Photo courtesy Milwaukee Public Museum.

Spectacular scenery surrounds places where Ice Age fossils
erode from buttes and gullies. Courtesy Badlands National
Park.

Southwest

Museum of Northern Arizona
Fort Valley Road
Flagstaff, Arizona 86001
602-779-1527

Open all year. Admission fee. Special programs.

Although this museum focuses on Southwest Indians, its prehistoric animal collection includes an early bird-hipped dinosaur. First described in 1981, *Scutellosaurus,* which has a row of bony studs guarding its back, is the only known armored dinosaur of this type. A long tail for balancing and long arms that may have served as extra legs made this four-foot-long herbivore swift and agile. It must have been able to wheel and dodge, outdistance, and fend off predators. Flagstaff has one of just two scutellosaurs in the country.

Museum of Paleontology
Earth Sciences Building
University of California
Berkeley, California 94720
510-642-1821

Open year round. Free admission. Call for special programs.

This is an active university museum with many special programs for the community and a strong collection of vertebrate and invertebrate fossils, including Triassic reptiles and *Dilophosaurus.* Perhaps as sexual advertisement, *Dilophosaurus,* the "two-ridged" lizard, has twin bony crests along its snout. Twenty feet long and strongly muscled, it used its terrible teeth and claws to strike out at the huge, plant-browsing dinosaurs of the Jurassic. The museum also features excellent visiting programs such as Dinamation.

Natural History Museum of Los Angeles County
900 Exposition Boulevard
Los Angeles, California 90007
213-744-3466

Located in Exposition Park. Open year round. Admission fee. Call for special programs.

See a huge three-toed dinosaur footprint made more than 100 million years ago; let your children make crayon rubbings of fossils embedded in stone. The Natural History Museum of L.A. County is California's largest and most-visited museum, and began building a new dinosaur exhibition hall in 1991. The museum contains the largest cataloged vertebrate fossil collection in North America and also operates the George C. Page Museum at the La Brea Tar Pits (next entry).

Crane your neck. "Wow . . . that's huge! Is it real?" A 72-foot *Mamenchisaurus* that once tipped the scales at 30 to 40 tons spans an entire wall. A duckbill fends off a fierce *Allosaurus* attack. *Triceratops* and *Stegosaurus* skeletons browse among marine mosasaurs and a pterosaur with a 23-foot wingspan.

L.A. also has a toothy tyrannosaur skull, one of the few specimens of this popular, scarce dinosaur. *Tyrannosaurus rex* fires the imagination: 6-inch serrated teeth, 6-ton size, 40 feet of carnivore. The favorite of every small boy, his likeness glowers at you in many museums and dinosaur parks, but a real skull is very unusual. *T. rex* has even starred in movies made in nearby Hollywood, vying with King Kong for Fay Wray's favors or smashing Tokyo as Godzilla. Pretty good for an animal that lived 68 million years ago.

T. rex's distinctive adaptations let us know just what he was up to back then. The combination of a strong skull, neck, and jaw with those incredible teeth, binocular vision, and swift, agile hind limbs made him an awesome predator. Scientists have theorized that the

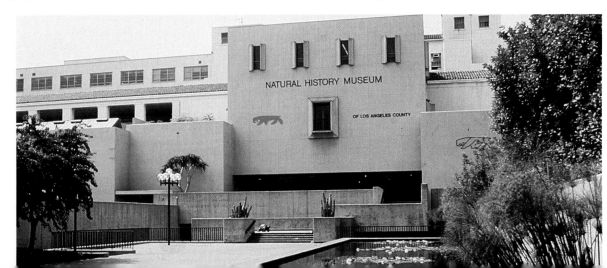

tyrannosaur, a late Cretaceous dinosaur, hunted not the huge *Diplodocus* (which had long been extinct) but fast, horned, elephant-sized *Triceratops*. In 1992 paleontologists in Wyoming uncovered part of the skeleton of a *Triceratops* that exhibits evidence of having been attacked and perhaps killed and eaten by a tyrannosaur, a broken tooth of which was found among the bones. This is the first direct evidence that these formidable horned dinosaurs actually fell victim to the fearsome tyrannosaurs. Moving in swiftly, *T. rex* could cut a wound a yard long and a foot deep – a single giant death bite.

Like most predators at the top of the food chain, *T. rex* was relatively rare. Parts of less than a dozen individuals have been found. The most recent, best preserved and most complete tyrannosaur fossil found to date turned up in the Black Hills of South Dakota in 1992. This tyrannosaur, named "Sue," is at this writing the focus of a custody suit involving the F.B.I., various government agencies and a private, commericial dealer in fossils charged with illegally acquiring the fossil skeleton from Federal land. Los Angeles joins New York's American Museum of Natural History, the Carnegie in Pittsburgh, The Academy of Natural Sciences in Philadelphia (a cast), and the Tyrrell in Alberta in hosting *Tyrannosaurus rex* skeletons, and they are much more popular today than they were when they roamed western North America.

George C. Page Museum of La Brea Discoveries
5801 Wilshire Boulevard
Los Angeles, California 90036
213-936-2230

Seven miles west of downtown Los Angeles in Hancock Park. Open year round. Admission fee. Call for special programs.

Watch the cleaning, identifying, and cataloging of tar pit fossils in the glass-walled paleontology laboratory. Pit your strength against the tar pit, pulling handles submerged in tar, and learn why those who dropped in for a visit at La Brea seldom left. See the skeletons of a saber-toothed cat and the La Brea Woman (the only human skeleton recovered from the tar pits) turn to fully fleshed models. And touch the massive, asphalt-soaked bone of a giant ground sloth. For two months each summer, visitors can watch the actual excavation at Pit 91 where scientists are recovering both plants and animals from 10,000 to 40,000 years ago.

In the city of Los Angeles, surrounded by sky-scrapers, is one of the richest stores of Pleistocene fossils in the world. Although not unique to California – there are other asphalt pits in Peru and the Caucasus – La Brea is a window on the past in North America. Explorer José Martinez described the tar pits in 1792: ". . . a great lake of pitch in which bubbles or blisters are continuously exploding. . . . In hot

(Left) The Natural History Museum of Los Angeles County, California.

(Above) Much more popular today than 100 million years ago is the fierce and predatory *T. rex*. Courtesy Natural History Museum of Los Angeles County.

weather animals have been seen to sink in it, and when they tried to escape, they were unable to do so because their feet were stuck, and the lake swallowed them. After many years their bones have come up through the holes as if petrified."

The tar pits were both treacherous and deceiving. In the rainy season, water covered the asphalt; water birds landed and became stuck in the tar. In the summer, leaves and dust disguised the pool. Most of the trapped vertebrate animals were carnivores, both mammals and scavenger birds, attracted by the carrion of other luckless animals. Big cats, dire wolves, and condors are common. In all, more than 40,000 plants and animals were trapped in the sticky asphalt, which preserved the hard parts of the creatures: bones, beaks, nails, and teeth.

California Academy of Sciences
Golden Gate Park
San Francisco, California 94118-4599
415-750-7145

Open year round. Admission fee. Call for information about special programs.

Come view ancient seas and the strange creatures lurking there. Meet their living descendants face to face. Stroll through primeval forests, but beware of animated beasts that creep and do battle there. Tremble beneath the 30-foot wingspan of a *Quetzalcoatlus* and touch fossils that are millions of years old. Trace the changes in dinosaurs as they move onto land, begin to eat plants, and learn to walk on two legs. Take a closer look at this amazing planet to see how continents, seas, and the life among them changed over time. Then test your new knowledge about evolution on interactive computers. . . .

All this and more awaits you as you walk with your family through 3.5 billion years of evolution in "Life through Time," described by the National Science Foundation as the world's finest exhibit on evolution. More than sixty displays show land movements and climatic changes as well as ancient plants and animals and their modern descendants. Divided into five major categories—Lines of Evidence, Early Life in the Sea, the Transition to Land, the Age of Mammals, and the Age of Reptiles—the exhibit includes computers,

models, fossils, and videos to make your trip through time as exciting as possible.

University of Colorado Museum
Broadway
Boulder, Colorado 80309
719-492-6165

Located between 15th and 16th Streets in downtown Boulder. Open year round. Free admission. Call for special programs.

Features vertebrate and invertebrate fossils and Jurassic dinosaurs.

Denver Museum of Natural History
2001 Colorado Boulevard
Denver, Colorado 80205
303-322-7009

Open year round. Admission fee. Call for special programs.

A life-sized cast of a *T. rex* skull and an entire skeleton pose before a mural depicting this predator in gruesome action as you enter the museum. The great curving tusks of an Imperial mammoth unearthed in Nebraska loom over your head. Spectacular mounted skeletons of rhinoceroses, mastodons, bison, horses, saber-toothed cats, and dire wolves challenge you in the Fossil Mammal Hall.

The glass-walled Earth Sciences Laboratories let you in on the secrets of paleontologists. A video microscope shows scientists chipping away millions of years of rock from bones and other fossils. Current work includes molding and casting plesiosaur and dinosaur materials and the preparation of *Coelophysis* and fossil mammals for display. An extensive fossil exhibit hall, planned for opening in 1995, will feature both vertebrates and invertebrates, walk-through habitat dioramas, and interactive components. Each year the Denver adds new specimens of dinosaurs and prehistoric mammals to its extensive collections through fieldwork and donations.

In 1937 a high school class on a field trip discovered the *Stegosaurus* that is now exhibited at the Denver Museum along with over ninety skeletons of fossilized

Life in ancient seas. Photo by Susan Middleton; courtesy California Academy of Sciences.

T. rex and his portrait greet you at the Denver Museum of Natural History. Photo by G. Hall.

mammals, reptiles, amphibians, and fishes. One of the most widespread dinosaurs, the *Stegosaurus* has stumped scientists since O.C. Marsh first discovered it in 1877. Its massive, narrow body is crested with a bony row of plates, arranged in single file or in pairs — scientists can't decide which — from spiky tail to tiny head. Those crests are a puzzle: were they brightly colored decorations to impress other stegosaurs? weapons of defense (but why only along the back)? Or were they Jurassic solar panels to regulate body temperature?

And what about the brain? Thinking was a luxury no sauropod could afford. Lumbering around (*Stegosaurus* was probably about as agile as a box turtle) and an occasional dinner date was about as intellectual as he could get. With a smaller brain than a kitten, *Stegosaurus* had a sacral spinal cord enlargement about twenty times the size of its brain just to operate its massive hind end and war-club tail. This "dual brain" inspired Bert L. Taylor of the *Chicago Tribune* to write the following (somewhat inaccurate) poem in 1912:

Behold the mighty dinosaur,
Famous in prehistoric lore.
Not only for his power and strength
But also for his intellectual length.
You will observe by these remains
The creature had two sets of brains —
One in his head (the usual place),
The other at his spinal base.
Thus he could reason "A priori"
As well as "A posteriori."
No problem bothered him a bit;
He made both head and tail of it.
So wide was he, so wide and solemn,
Each thought filled just a spinal column.
If one brain found the pressure strong
It passed a few ideas along.
If something slipped his forward mind
'Twas rescued by the one behind.
And if in error he was caught
He had a saving afterthought.
As he thought twice before he spoke
He had no judgment to revoke.
Thus he could think without congestion
Upon both sides of every question.
Oh, gaze upon this model beast,
Defunct ten million years at least.*

* Actually defunct at least 135 million years.

Garden Park Fossil Area
The Garden Park Paleontology Society
P.O. Box 313
Cañon City, Colorado 81215-0313

Located in central Colorado. Write for information and programs.

In the 1870s, enormously important fossil finds in the American West captured the imaginations, pocket-books, and energies of two paleontologists who would spend the rest of their lives as rivals in search of the fame and glory of dinosaur discoveries: Othniel C. Marsh of Yale – determined, cold-eyed, and resent-ful – and Edward Drinker Cope of Philadelphia – brilliant and impetuous. Guns, bribes, aliases, vituper-ative newspaper attacks, government and academic lobbying, spying and deception were all part of the game. Despite their rivalry, this period saw tremen-dous advances in uncovering information about the Age of Dinosaurs.

As the 1870s Indian wars raged, buffalo were slaughtered, and land was fenced for farming and graz-ing, paleontologists staked their claims. The Morrison Formation in Colorado, Dinosaur Triangle in Utah, Como in Wyoming, and the Judith River in Montana became the regions of the dinosaur hunters. From rude shacks on windswept plains they painstakingly ex-cavated huge bones of entire dinosaurs and shipped them back east despite incredible difficulties and hard-ships. Snowstorms, Indians, lack of supplies, and in-adequate help did not deter them. While Custer's troops clashed with the Sioux at the Little Bighorn, not many miles away Cope was digging dinosaurs at the Judith River, convinced that Custer would keep the Sioux occupied.

When the smoke cleared, hundreds of new species had been cataloged. These early field-workers made major finds such as the colossal skeletons of sauropods like *Apatosaurus* (*Brontosaurus*) and *Diplodocus*. They found the small predator *Coelurus* and the great car-nivorous *Allosaurus*. Thanks to their perseverance, *Stegosaurus*, *Pterodactyl*, and *Triceratops* would take their places in newly built American museums, pale-ontology in the field would become professional, and new theories would expand our understanding of the Mesozoic Era.

Before Cope and Marsh began hunting fossils, only nine dinosaur species were known in North America; between them they added 136 more. They described more than 1800 new genera or species. Cope and Marsh finally died, bitter enemies to the end. But they left behind a wonderful legacy of dinosaurs that cap-tured the public imagination, and the men they had hired and trained set out on new explorations.

Garden Park is the site where the "Great Dinosaur Race" between Cope and Marsh began; the two had excavations only a short distance from each other here, and no other geologic site better illustrates the famous Cope–Marsh rivalry. Together with the Bureau of Land Management and the Denver Museum of Natural His-tory, the Garden Park Paleontology Society is raising money to preserve this area, build a visitor center, further research, and educate the public. Programs in paleontology certify volunteers to explore for fossils here.

In 1991, on the last day of an expedition of the Den-ver Museum of Natural Science, a volunteer amateur paleontologist unearthed the huge fossil skeleton of a yet-to-be-identified 70-foot dinosaur. Other trained volunteers have found additional dinosaur fossils, fos-silized footprints, and the remains of non-dinosaur rep-tiles to carry on the Cope–Marsh tradition at Garden Park.

Stegosaurus and company in Dinosaur Hall. Courtesy Denver Museum of Natural History.

Museum of Western Colorado

248 South Fourth Street
Box 20000-5020
Grand Junction, Colorado 81502
303-242-0971

Located in downtown Grand Junction in western Colorado. Both the museum and Dinosaur Valley are open all year.

This museum manages three natural resource areas that interpret local fossil history: Riggs Hill is the site where the *Brachiosaurus* was excavated in 1900; the *Apatosaurus* was unearthed at nearby Dinosaur Hill; and Rabbit Hill is the site of ongoing fossil digs and a program run by Dinamation (contact Michael Perry, Dinamation International Society, P.O. Box 307, Fuita, CO 81521). Each of these sites has self-guided trails where you can see quarries or bones and fossils in the rocks.

Located two blocks from the main museum, Dinosaur Valley explores the science of paleontology. Fossils of worldwide importance and exhibits on pioneer researchers, ancient trackways, and the fossil-rich Western Slope explain long-ago worlds. Look in on an active paleontology lab. Dinosaur Valley also features realistic animated dinosaurs that stomp and roar.

Florissant Fossil Beds National Monument

P.O. Box 185
Florissant, Colorado 80816

Located in a small mountain community 35 miles west of Colorado Springs. Admission fee. Programs year round. Write for information. Few accommodations in the area, access by car.

The finest insect and plant fossils of the Oligocene Epoch found anywhere in the world are preserved in this 6,000-acre monument. Year-round hiking, self-guided trails, cross-country skiing, horseback riding,

nature walks, and educational programs are available for visitors. The park is filled with wildflowers, rolling grassy hills and ridges covered with blue spruce and aspen, and abundant wildlife.

The fossils here are preserved in the sedimentary rocks of ancient Lake Florissant. Volcanic ash carried by the wind trapped insects, spiders, and leaves in the lake where they settled to the bottom in the fine ash and became fossils. Beneath the rolling meadowlands, impressions of dragonflies, beetles, ants, butterflies, spiders, fish, mammals, plants, and birds that lived here almost 35 million years ago are perfectly preserved. Visitors can view excavated fossils in the visitor center.

Berlin-Ichthyosaur State Park

Route 1, Box 32
Austin, Nevada 89310
702-867-3001

Located in south central Nevada. The park is open year round, but extreme winter weather may prevent travel.

Hiking, camping, nature walks, guided tours of the Fossil Shelter, and a Nevada ghost mining town beckon explorers at Berlin-Ichthyosaur State Park. A self-guided tour of the quarry lets you discover the remains of nine icthyosaurs left in the rock.

Over countless millions of years, icthyosaur ancestors — their name means "fish lizard" — evolved into fishlike reptiles of the sea. Streamlined bodies with broad paddles for steering, balance, and braking and long-toothed snouts for capturing prey made them the terror of Mesozoic oceans. Icthyosaurs surfaced to breathe air through lungs and gave live birth, maintaining and hatching eggs within the mother's body much as sharks do today. Some forty specimens have been found in the park.

This hornet once buzzed above the waters of Lake Florissant. Photo by Walt Saenger; courtesy Florissant Fossil Beds.

Florence Hawley Ellis Museum of Anthropology
Ghost Ranch Conference Center
Abiquiu, New Mexico 87510
505-685-4333

Open year round. Free admission.

Working out of the ancient desert town of Abiquiu, New Mexico, in 1881, David Baldwin shipped off some "small and tender" finds to Philadelphia, where Edward Drinker Cope promptly dubbed them *Coelophysis* — "hollow nature" — because the bones were hollow. After the discovery of these lightweight, graceful lizard-hipped dinosaurs, which relied on speed for catching prey (perhaps dragonflies or young dinosaurs), these rather interesting creatures were forgotten for sixty years. Then in 1947, researchers from the American Museum of Natural History staying at Ghost Ranch in Abiquiu unearthed an exciting jumble of *Coelophysis* bones — all ages: legs, tails, heads all piled together.

These are some of the most complete dinosaur skeletons ever discovered, and the variety of ages in the group gives us the best information ever unearthed concerning one species of Triassic dinosaur. Within the delicate hollow bones of two of the skeletons were the whole remains of tiny *Coelophysis* individuals. Were these unborn fetuses? Did *Coelophysis* give live birth? Or are these the remains of some Triassic cannibalistic feast (could the little creatures have been swallowed whole without a single bone being broken)?

Visit these enigmatic dinosaurs at Ghost Ranch where they were discovered and puzzle over the questions they pose.

Parasaurolophus once again forages in the wetlands of New Mexico. Photo by Ron Behman; courtesy New Mexico Museum of Natural History (next page).

New Mexico Museum of Natural History
1801 Mountain Road, N.W.
Old Town
Albuquerque, New Mexico 87104
505-841-8836

Open year round. Admission fee. Call for special programs.

Take a trip on the Evolator Time Machine through 38 million years of New Mexico's geologic and evolutionary history. Trace the creation of the universe from the Big Bang to present-day solar systems. See continents grow and divide as mighty oceans swell and tectonic plates collide with ripping force. Follow the struggle for survival as cells multiply and triumph. Watch sharks circle ominously and living fossils explore their tide-pool world. Bone up on some of New Mexico's largest and most impressive citizens, now extinct: giant flying pterosaurs, brachiosaurs, and *Coelophysis.* Cool, moist air glistens in the soft sunlight of a living coal forest while the evolution of mammals comes to life. As you descend into the earth in the Age of Volcanoes, the heat is on. Walls roar with burning rocks, corridors tremble with hissing steam and flowing lava, and fire spikes the air as you walk through a volcano. Then take a cool trip through New Mexico's Ice Age and visit an underground cave world.

In addition to the Time Machine, New Mexico houses many conventional dinosaur exhibits including bronze models of *Pentaceratops* and *Albertosaurus* as well as murals, fossils, and skeletal casts and models of other dinosaurs. Of special interest is the fossil material of *Seismosaurus,* the longest animal that ever lived. The "earthquake lizard," discovered in 1985, is estimated to be well over 100 feet in length and is still being excavated in northwest New Mexico.

Oklahoma Museum of Natural History
University of Oklahoma
1335 Asp Avenue
Norman, Oklahoma 73019
405-325-4712

Open year round. Free admission. Call for special programs.

Fossils here include *Acrocanthosaurus.* Forty feet long with a healthy appetite and 12-inch spines along its backbone, this carnivore once roamed Oklahoma looking for a meal. The spines may have been for protection, sexual advertising, or solar heating (and cooling) to regulate body temperature.

NOTE: If you are planning a dinosaur vacation trip anywhere in **Utah**, call 801-789-4002 for Dinoland Travel Information, a service provided by the Utah Field House of Natural History State Park.

Dinosaur National Monument
P.O. Box 128
Jensen, Utah 84035
801-789-2115

Located near the Colorado border, east of Vernal and north of Jensen, Utah. Open year round. Camping facilities available.

This large desert park encompasses many square miles of scenic trails, rivers for fishing and rafting, rocks with petroglyphs, unusual geologic formations, and wildlife areas. The highlight for dinosaur fans is the covered Dinosaur Quarry where more than 1,600 bones have been uncovered and left in place to form a unique exhibit – a wall of dinosaurs from the Jurassic Morrison Formation, accompanied by dinosaur models, mounted skeletons, and a window to the paleontology lab. Well-known late-Jurassic dinosaurs such as *Allosaurus, Apatosaurus, Diplodocus, Camptosaurus* and *Stegosaurus* once hung out here.

You can find fossils yourself in the wall of the Dinosaur Quarry. Courtesy Dinosaur National Monument.

Mill Canyon Dinosaur Trail and Potash Road Dinosaur Tracks

c/o Grand Resource Area
Bureau of Land Management
885 S. Sand Flats Road
Moab, Utah 84532
801-259-8193

Mill Canyon is on a dirt road off US Highway 191, 13 miles north of Moab; Potash Road Tracks are on State Highway 279. Write the address above for a brochure and map.

See Morrison Formation dinosaur fossils and petrified wood in a natural setting. This outdoor museum operates on the honor system: visitors may look and touch, but collecting is not allowed. The dinosaur tracks at Potash Road can be viewed by scope or you can hike up to see them. Other dinosaur tracks may be seen at Red Fleet State Park north of Vernal and Warner Valley near St. George (managed by the BLM).

Cleveland-Lloyd Dinosaur Quarry

c/o Price River Resource Area
Bureau of Land Management
900 North 7th East
Price, Utah 84501
801-637-4584

Located thirty miles south of Price, Utah, on State Highway 10. Open daily from Memorial Day to Labor Day, weekends the rest of the year. Primitive camping available.

Since 1928, excavations have unearthed over 17,000 dinosaur bones at Cleveland-Lloyd, and *Allosaurus* skeletons have been found in great abundance here. Quarry tours originate at the Visitors Center.

(Above) *Stegosaurus* greets you at the Dinosaur Quarry, Dinosaur National Monument, Utah.

(Right) Some stars of the dino collection at the Utah Museum of Natural History.

College of Eastern Utah Prehistoric Museum
451 East 400 North
Price, Utah 84501
801-637-5060

Located at the corner of Main and Second East. Open year round. Donations are suggested.

Cretaceous dinosaur tracks and reconstructed Jurassic skeletons from the Cleveland-Lloyd Quarry. Included are *Allosaurus, Stegosaurus, Camptosaurus,* and *Camarasaurus. Utahraptor,* a 20-foot, one-ton dinosaur dubbed "superslasher" was unearthed in eastern Utah by a C. of E.U. laboratory staff member in 1991. The 15-inch-long raised claw on each hind foot made this swift predator, which hunted in packs 125 million years ago, perhaps the deadliest predator the world has ever seen. Swifter and more deadly than even the fearsome tyrannosaur, the utahraptor could disembowel a much larger dinosaur with a single kick. The utahraptor is destined for display in the College of Eastern Utah Prehistoric Museum.

Utah Museum of Natural History
University of Utah
215 South 1350 East
Salt Lake City, Utah 84112
801-581-6927

Located on President's Circle on the University of Utah campus. Open year round. Admission fee. Call for special programs.

In the Ice Age Discovery Room, saber-toothed cats and dire wolves stalk before a mural of the Salt Lake Valley. A muskox and giant bison graze. Scheduled to join them are a Huntington mammoth and a giant sloth skeleton. Casts and models of the bones are made and assembled in the exhibit so visitors can watch and ask questions. Children can take part in the simulated excavation of a mastodon, field trips, and other special programs.

Four dinosaurs tower above you – a *Stegosaurus,* a *Camptosaurus* and two allosaurs. Utah is in the process of excavating dinosaurs from the Long Walk Quarry –

dinosaurs that supply a missing link between those of the Morrison Formation 150 million years ago and the Mesa Verde group of about 80 million years ago. Predators with 4-inch serrated teeth — a transition between *Allosaurus* and *T. rex* — and huge brontosaur-like herbivores have been found here for the first time. These early Cretaceous finds will swell the museum's collection, which also includes material from Dinosaur National Monument and the Cleveland-Lloyd Quarry. Keep your eye on this museum; its collection is growing fast.

Brigham Young University Earth Science Museum
1683 North Canyon Road
Provo, Utah 84602
801-378-3680

Located on campus west of the BYU football stadium. Open year round.

Ranked among the top five collections of Jurassic dinosaurs in the world, BYU has an extremely active program, including many activities for children. Thousands of dinosaur bones are stored under the BYU Cougar Stadium bleachers. Known as the "bleacher creatures," they are awaiting funds for study and display. This is a small museum with a lot to offer.

Fossils and casts of *Ultrasaurus* and *Supersaurus,* two of the largest dinosaurs ever, join *T. rex, Triceratops,* and a 50-foot crocodile. Kids can touch dinosaur fossils, put their heads in a *T. rex* mouth, watch museum personnel study and prepare fossils, and test their knowledge about dinosaurs on interactive TV. See the oldest dinosaur egg ever found and an X ray of the embryo inside. This tiny dinosaur died just before it hatched; it even has two fossilized baby teeth.

Utah Field House of Natural History State Park
235 East Main
Vernal, Utah 84078
801-789-3799

Open year round. Admission fee.

Exhibits include dinosaur and large mammal fossils. Adjacent Dinosaur Gardens include both dinosaurs and prehistoric mammals in lifelike settings.

(Right) At the Tyrrell Museum of Palaeontology in Drumheller, Alberta, Canada, you can design and field test your own dinosaur.

(Left) Preparing a fossil turtle. Courtesy Carter County Museum, Ekalaka, Montana (described on page 94).

Northwest

Royal Tyrrell Museum of Palaeontology
P.O. Box 7500
Drumheller, Alberta, Canada T0J 0Y0
403-823-7707

Open year round with many special summer programs. Admission fee. About 90 minutes by car from Calgary and 3½ hours from Edmonton.

Situated in the spectacular Red Deer River Valley, home of some of the most productive dinosaur hunting grounds in the world, the entire Royal Tyrrell Museum is devoted to paleontology. Walk through the Royal Tyrrell and the past comes alive. Discover the story written in the rocks of the surrounding badlands: chapters of birth, death, struggle, and survival. Exhibits of over 800 fossil specimens — including thirty-five complete dinosaur skeletons — let you experience 3.5 billion years of Earth's history. Most of these dinosaurs and fossils were excavated along the Red Deer River during the Great Canadian Dinosaur Rush which pitted Barnum Brown of the American Museum of Natural History against Charles Sternberg from the Canadian Geological Survey in a friendly rivalry to collect the finest fossil specimens to be found in this area.

Another special feature is the Palaeoconservatory housing more than 110 species of plants, descendants

of the flora in Alberta during the Age of Dinosaurs. In the Nova Room you can discover what it would be like to be on a bone dig, examine fossilized insects through a microscope, get your hands on original fossils and casts, and learn how to pronounce those lo-o-ong dinosaur names. Computer aficionados can "build" and test their own dinosaurs or access an encyclopedia of dinosaurs on one of eighteen video screens. More than half a million visitors a year make the trip to Alberta to visit the Tyrrell, one of the most creative and educational museums in the world.

Tyrrell Museum of Palaeontology Field Station
c/o Royal Tyrrell Museum of Palaeontology
Box 7500
Drumheller, Alberta, Canada T0J 0Y0
403-378-4342

Located in Dinosaur Provincial Park, north of Brooks, Alberta. Open year round. Donations welcome.

Step out of the stark badlands of today's Dinosaur Provincial Park and into the world of 75 million years ago when dinosaurs roamed a prehistoric world of rivers, marshes, and forests. The Field Station programs and exhibits bring to life the discovery of more than thirty-five species of dinosaurs. Watch videos in the theater on collecting dinosaurs and get a first-hand look at staff working on fossils in the preparation lab.

Dinosaur Provincial Park
P.O. Box 60
Patricia, Alberta, Canada T0J 2K0
403-378-4342

Open year round. Call for special programs. Camping available.

Dinosaur Provincial Park not only has one of the world's most important deposits of fossilized bone (some of which can be seen in situ) but also 25 square miles of spectacular badlands to hike, canoe, and explore. Approximately thirty-six different species of dinosaurs have been found in the rocks of the Park. Many other kinds of fossil animals are also found here including turtles, crocodiles, fish, flying reptiles, salamanders, and small mammals.

Idaho Museum of Natural History
Campus Box 8096
Idaho State University
Pocatello, Idaho 83209
208-236-3168

Open year round. Admission fee to some exhibits. Call for special programs.

Highlights include Dinamation exhibits, mobile classrooms, and the Hall of Discovery. Emphasis is on Great Basin and northern Rocky Mountains vertebrate paleontology.

Museum of the Rockies
600 West Kagy
Bozeman, Montana 59717
406-994-2251

Open Year round. Admission fee. Call for special programs.

Home of the *Maiasaura,* the "good mother" dinosaur and her clutch of eggs — a major discovery that vastly altered our concepts of dinosaur life-styles. In the summer of 1978, Jack Horner and Bob Makela found fifteen fossilized dinosaur babies in a nest of mud in Montana. The nest was about seven feet across and three feet deep. Other nests later turned up containing babies that ranged from about 21 inches to 7 feet in length. The babies had worn teeth, evidence that they had been eating for some time. Eventually an adult skull was found and Horner estimated the adult, a kind of hadrosaur, at about 27 to 34 feet long. Horner named the dinosaur *Maiasaura* — good mother lizard. Obviously, these great big mamas cared for their babies: the babies' worn teeth and the nests with varying sizes of babies suggest that the parents brought berries, seeds, and leaves to feed their offspring until they grew to a self-sufficient size.

Nests were found about the length of an adult apart, in groups, so there must have been breeding colonies. Nests were found in several strata, suggesting that dinosaurs returned to breeding grounds year after year. And since fossilized members of this dinosaur tribe were also found in coastal and upland areas, it appears these dinosaurs migrated at egg-laying times, perhaps

away from the wet areas and out of the range of deadly predators. Nesting in colonies would have given them the added protection of group lookouts, as well.

Only the bottoms of the eggs remain in some nests, half-buried in mud. Perhaps the dinosaur mothers gathered vegetation and tucked it around the eggs, letting it warm them as it rotted (a trick still used by crocodiles and some birds today).

Since the hadrosaurs were widespread dinosaurs — a specimen found in New Jersey was the first dinosaur skeleton assembled — their nesting tactics must have been successful. The instinct to nest in colonies, to migrate to nesting spots, to build circular nests, to incubate eggs with vegetation, and to feed and care for the young lives on today in those familiar dinosaur relatives, the birds.

The duckbilled *Anatosaurus* may have serenaded the Montana skies with tunes bellowed through loose nose flaps. Photo by Marshall Lambert; courtesy Carter County Museum, Ekalaka, Montana (described on page 94).

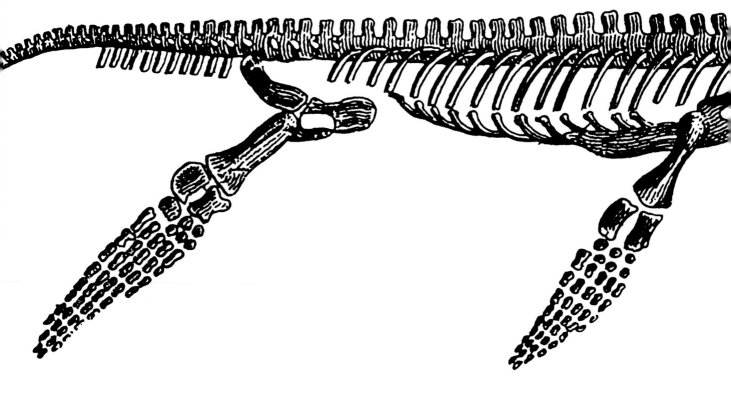

Carter County Museum
100 Main Street
Ekalaka, Montana 59324
406-775-6886

Located in the southeast corner of Montana, bordering the Dakotas and Wyoming. Open year round. Free admission.

Literally a *fossil museum,* the walls of the Carter County Museum are built of petrified wood. Against this unique backdrop are fossils found in the Ekalaka area, including a full mount of the duckbilled *Anatosaurus,* dinosaur tracks, and skulls of *Triceratops* and *Nanotyrannus,* the pygmy tyrannosaur. A huge fossil turtle rubs elbows with mastodon and mammoth bones, teeth and tusks, and an Ice Age bison skull. Children can actually get their hands on fossilized dinosaur bones at this delightful little museum.

John Day Fossil Beds National Monument
420 West Main Street
John Day, Oregon 97845

Operated by the National Park Service. Write the Superintendent at this address for more information. Located in central Oregon. Open year round. No camping in the park.

Covering more than 14,000 acres, the John Day landscape includes badlands, palisades, scenic drives, painted hills, overlooks, and interpretive trails. Visitors can follow trails into the badlands of John Day Valley or examine fossil displays at the visitor's center while scientists continue field investigation and the painstaking analysis of the monument's vast stratified fossil record.

The badlands of John Day Valley are fossil beds, the fossil remains of jungles, savannas, and woodlands that flourished here during 40 million years in the Cenozoic Era when ancestral horses, elephants, bears, rhinos, and cats roamed, volcanoes erupted, and the landscape changed from rain forest to desert. Although today there are only bears and mountain lions in North America, at the end of the Pleistocene, cave lions, saber-toothed cats, and great short-faced bears ranged over much of the continent. The cave lions crossed the

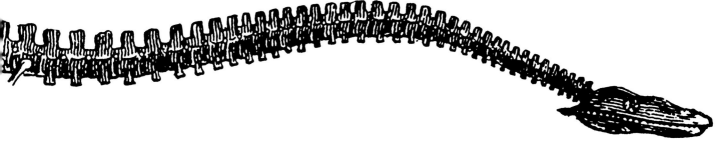

land bridge from Siberia and finally reached Peru. No other land mammal before man was so widely spread on five continents and adapted to such a wide variety of climates. Brainier than even present-day lions, these large cats had a social life-style and hunted in prides. The cave lion was a supercarnivore: large, strong, and intelligent. Males measured up to 8½ feet from the nose to the base of the tail. Like modern lions, they had dark manes, tufted tails, and possibly spots like lion cubs today. These magnificent creatures preyed on the huge herds of horses, camels, and bison that roamed throughout North America, and remains have been found in forty states from Alaska to Florida.

Saber-tooths (or smilodonts) fed on ground sloths, mammoths, and mastodons. Shorter and heavier than a modern African lion, saber-toothed cats were deliberate animals that relied on their powerful paws and long, swordlike canines, which protruded from their jaws, to kill their prey. Too stocky for speed, their hunting style involved ambush rather than chase. However, the large number of remains with injured bones suggests they were very aggressive. Everything in the saber-tooth skull was designed around those 8-inch ivories: the brain case was smaller than that of modern lions; the jaws opened extra wide to allow the cats to slit open the necks or bellies of their prey. Saber-tooths ranged far and wide in the grasslands of North America, and died out when many of the large mammals vanished.

Bears of various sizes and habits also roamed throughout North America. The great short-faced bear was the largest bear ever, more than three feet taller at the shoulder than a modern grizzly and topping the scales at 15,000 pounds. This carnivore must have been a formidable predator, relatively long-legged and fleet-footed for a bear, with long ursine claws and plenty of paw power. Human hunting, competition from what became modern bears, and the dying out of prey are all possible causes of their extinction.

Fossil Butte National Monument
P.O. Box 527
Kemmerer, Wyoming 83101
307-877-4455

Open all year. Write or call for special events and programs.

Today Fossil Butte National Monument is an arid landscape of flat-topped buttes and ridges, dominated by sagebrush and other desert shrubs. It's hard to imagine that 50 million years ago this was a lake teeming with life in a subtropical climate. But the evidence lies clearly in the rocks all around you. In the 200–300 feet of sediment at the top of Fossil Butte are the fossils of turtles, fish, rays, snails, crocodiles, and birds. Beautifully preserved fish with delicate fins, tail rays, and scales are entombed in thinly layered sediments recording the abundant life and ecology of the ancient lake. Nearby are quarries where scientists have unearthed fossilized horses and other early mammals. The visitor center museum exhibits many of the finds and offers guides and brochures about the area. There are hiking trails through the fossil quarries.

The Geological Museum
University of Wyoming Department
of Geology & Geophysics
Laramie, Wyoming 82071-3006
307-766-4218

Open weekdays all year and occasionally on weekends. Free admission. Educational programs.

Exhibits of vertebrate and invertebrate paleontology include an *Apatosaurus,* AKA *Brontosaurus.*

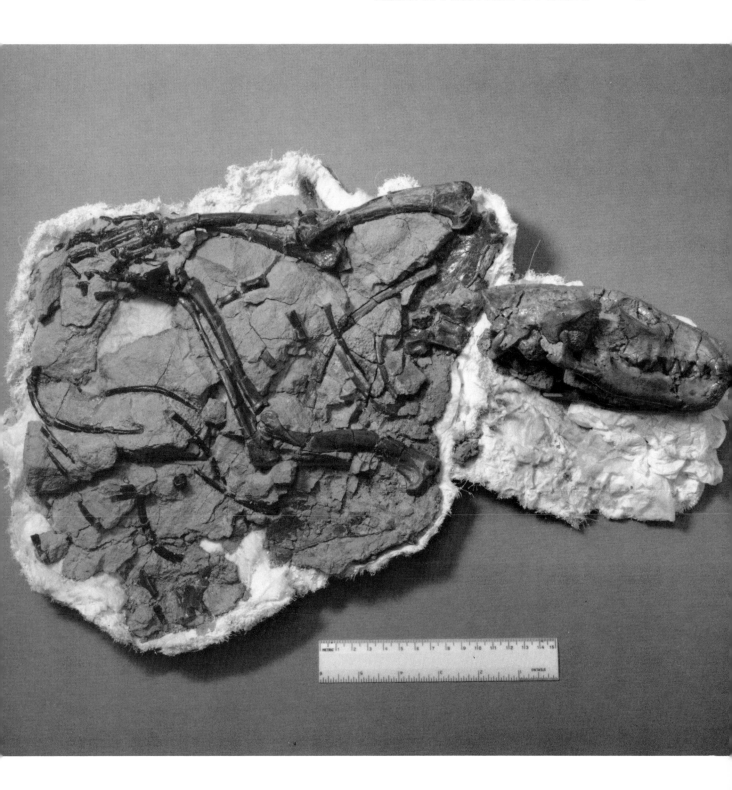

(Left) Fossil beds at Sheep Rock. (Above) A fossilized dog, 25 million years old, recovered at Sheep Rock. Photos courtesy John Day Fossil Beds.

7
Dinosaur Digs:
Volunteer Opportunities in Paleontology

Edmontosaurus fends off an *Allosaurus*. Courtesy Natural History Museum of Los Angeles County, California.

The listings included here are for recent programs, but volunteer opportunities change all the time. Call or write the organizations for information on current programs. Within sections, listed alphabetically by state unless otherwise noted.

BLM and National Parks

Federally run programs at sites managed by the Bureau of Land Management or the National Park Service offer volunteers many opportunities to get involved with field and museum work. These programs give students valuable experience in the field and on-the-job training. Retirees may be able to use their professional skills or may choose to try something new. Both summer-long and occasional positions are available. Usually you need to provide your own housing, food, and transportation.

Project Coordinator
U.S. Bureau of Land Management
1849 C Street, N.W., Room 3615
Washington, D.C. 20240
202-208-5261

Ages: 18 and up.

Qualifications: Some projects require special skills; others need only a willingness to work.

Costs: Occasionally volunteers are reimbursed for some expenses, but generally they are responsible for room, board, and travel.

The BLM manages land primarily in the western states of Alaska, Arizona, California, Colorado, Idaho, Montana, Nevada, New Mexico, Oregon, Utah, and Wyoming. Many of these are prime dinosaur fossil states where the BLM actually manages some of the sites. Varied opportunities. Write the Washington office or contact the individual state offices for volunteer opportunities.

Volunteers are needed to do research in museums. Courtesy American Museum of Natural History, New York.

Patricia Foulk, State Volunteer Coordinator
Bureau of Land Management/California
2800 Cottage Way
Sacramento, California 95825

Garden Park Paleontological Society
P.O. Box 313
Cañon City, Colorado 81215-0313
Attn: Cara Fisher

BLM of Colorado, in conjunction with the Garden Park Paleontological Society, is establishing a museum at Garden Park and much of the work is being done by volunteers. In 1991 a volunteer discovered a 70-foot dinosaur. Volunteers are needed on the Colorado site, and also for historical research at the American Museum of Natural History in New York City, the Peabody Museum in New Haven, Connecticut, and the Smithsonian in Washington, D.C.

Lorrene Schardt, State Volunteer Coordinator
BLM Montana State Office
Box 36800, 2222 North 32nd Street
Billings, Montana 59107
406-255-2827.

BLM uses volunteers both in the field and in museums in Montana.

Superintendent
U.S. National Park Service
Agate Fossil Beds National Monument
Post Office Box 27
Gering, Nebraska 69341
308-436-4340

Agate Fossil Beds is a site rich in Miocene mammal fossils. The park just recently opened a museum and is looking for volunteers to work in the museum and in the park.

BLM New Mexico State Office
1474 Rodeo Road, P.O. Box 27115
Santa Fe, New Mexico 87502-7115

Several New Mexico sites need volunteers for digs, monitoring, and data collection: Albuquerque (call Mike O'Neill at 505-479-8700), Las Cruces (call Mike Maloof at 505-525-8228); or for information on Southeastern New Mexico caving, archaeology, and paleontology call Paul Happel, Roswell District Office, at 505-622-9042.

Dinosaur National Monument
P.O. Box 128
Jensen, Utah 84035
801-789-2115

Call or write about their volunteer program.

Fossil Butte National Monument
P.O. Box 592
Kemmerer, Wyoming 83101-0592
307-877-4455

Call or write about their volunteer program.

* * *

The Dinosaur Society
P.O. Box 2098
New Bedford, Massachusetts 02741
508-997-2467

Offers field trips for families to dinosaur dig sites in North America and several overseas locations. The trips include digging and tours of the excavations.

The Student Conservation Association
Resource Assistant Program
P.O. Box 550
Charlestown, New Hampshire 03603
603-826-4301

Ages: High school through adult.

Qualifications vary.

Cost: Limited funds are available to offset expenses.

The SCA Resource Assistant Program matches volunteers with programs in the National Park Service, BLM, Fish and Wildlife Department, and so on. Most of the volunteers serve for twelve weeks, forty hours a week. Recent opportunities were at sites like Dinosaur National Monument, Florissant Fossil Beds National Monument, and Cleveland-Lloyd Dinosaur Quarry. Write for an extensive catalog of current listings.

The Dinosaur Quarry at Dinosaur National Monument, Jensen, Utah.

Vacations with Scientists in the Field

A number of organizations offer vacations throughout the world working with scientists in the field. Often your expenses are tax deductible as contributions to scientific research. Some family programs permit children as young as five to get involved. Usually you must provide your own transportation to the location of the dig and the organization provides daily ground transportation. Digging for dinosaurs is hot, dusty work, but if your family would like to work alongside a paleontologist uncovering real dinosaur or mammoth bones, call one of these organizations. (Listed alphabetically.)

Dinosaur Discovery Expeditions
Dinamation International Society
189-A Technology Drive
Irvine, California 92718
800-547-0503

Ages: Adult (ages 13 and up) and family programs (ages 5 and up).

Qualifications: Enthusiasm.

Costs: $695–1495; children $525; includes lodging, lunches in the field, equipment, daily ground transportation. You provide transportation to and from Grand Junction, Colorado, or Laramie, Wyoming, some meals and personal items.

Dinamation organizes adult and family dinosaur expeditions from 5 days to two weeks' duration, with opportunities to dig for dinosaur fossils, work in a paleontology lab, and assist well-known paleontologists in the Dinosaur Triangle area of eastern Utah, as well as the Colorado Badlands and Wyoming Highlands. Participants have unearthed *Apatosaurus, Allosaurus,* and *Stegosaurus* fossils on recent expeditions.

DINAMATION

A *Triceratops* browses peacefully among the swampy vegetation; its horns and strangely-ruffed, bony frill seem innocuous. Suddenly the creature stiffens, cocks its head and listens; its eyes roll. It stamps its foot and lets out a tremendous roar. Now the horns and armored plates are menacing. In the audience a little girl clutches her dad's pants leg and someone else lets out a nervous shriek; it seems so real.

This is Dinamation: robotic dinosaurs, prehistoric mammals, futuristic animals and sea creatures cropping up in museums large and small throughout the United States: Kalamazoo, Durham, Berkeley, Buffalo, Boston. Some of the creatures are animated; others are stationary outdoor models. Some are full-sized; others are reduced to fit the limitations of museum doorways and delivery truck beds. Wherever they go and whatever their size, these steel, aluminum, and rubber dinosaurs steal the show: attendance jumps three to fifteen times.

Dinamation provides a complete learning package with the robots, which "act" in skits that portray Mesozoic and Pleistocene dramas such as mama protecting her babies, three *Deinonychus* ("terrible claws") dining on a fallen dinosaur with a hopeful *Pterodactyl* hovering nearby, or an undulating mososaur in search of prey. The exhibits can also include stationary outdoor dinosaurs, newsletters, robotic dinosaurs kids can operate with a joystick, and plays. Dinamation publishes newsletters, sponsors digs, and supports museums.

For information on the nearest traveling exhibition and other information, call 1-800-547-0503.

Screen washing fossil fragments. Rushmore photo courtesy
of The Mammoth Site of Hot Springs, South Dakota.

Earthwatch
680 Mount Auburn Street, Box 403 N
Watertown, Massachusetts 02272
617-926-8200

Ages: 16 and up.

Qualifications: Enthusiasm and a stong back!

Costs: From $995–1295; includes room, board, and ground transportation. You provide transportation to the site and personal items.

Earthwatch assists scientific projects by locating paying volunteers for two- to three-week stints throughout the world. Recent paleontology projects included combing a fossil-rich site for fossilized sharks from a warm inland sea that lapped Montana's shores 320 million years ago, excavating mammoths from the Mammoth Hot Springs site in South Dakota, and exploring causes of dinosaur demise in Montana. Earthwatch also offers paleontology opportunities in other countries.

Foundation for Field Research
P.O. Box 2010
Alpine, California 91903
619-445-9364

Ages: 14–86. Children under 18 are welcome.

Qualifications: Enthusiasm and an eagerness to work.

Costs: $600 and up; includes contribution to the scientific project, room and board, field manager/cook, and ground transportation. You provide transportation to the site and personal gear.

The Foundation matches enthusiastic volunteers with scientists who need help with their projects throughout the world. Projects, scientists, and volunteers are carefully screened for the best match. Recent programs included searching for dinosaur fossils in the San Juan Basin in New Mexico and for Miocene mammals in Baja, California.

Four Corners School of Outdoor Education
East Route
Monticello, Utah 84535
801-587-2156

Ages: 14 and up

Qualifications and difficulty vary and are rated for each project.

Costs vary; $375 and up.

The Four Corners School offers outdoor opportunities for learning primarily in natural history, archaeology, and museum work rather than paleontology. They take small groups into the wilderness for learning/camping/adventure trips in the Colorado Plateau. College credit is available.

International Research Expeditions
140 University Drive
Menlo Park, California 94025
415-323-4228

Ages: No limits; discounts for families of three or more.

Qualifications: Enthusiasm.

Costs: $695 and up. Includes ground transportation, food and lodging, equipment and supplies. You provide transportation to the site and personal gear.

IRE brings together field research scientists and interested volunteers who want to assist. Recently they fielded an opportunity to dig dinosaurs in Montana with personnel from Northern Montana College and the Museum of the Rockies. Volunteers helped in removing *Albertosaurus* bones, cataloging finds, applying plaster casts for shipment, and prospecting for additional finds.

University Research Expeditions Program
University of California
Berkeley, California 94720
510-642-6586

Team up with professors from the University of California on various expeditions throughout the world. Programs vary and may or may not include paleontology. A brochure is available.

Bone preservation in progress. Rushmore photo courtesy of The Mammoth Site of Hot Springs, South Dakota.

Museums & Universities

Museums and universities also need paleontology volunteers for everything from acting as a docent on Sunday mornings to wrestling an *Albertosaurus* out of the Montana Badlands or cleaning bones with dental tools. The following list only scratches the surface. If you are interested in paleontology, get in touch with your local museum, park, or university and see what volunteer openings are available. If no programs are in place, start one. In many cases, volunteers have simply made opportunities for themselves. Students, retirees, and anyone who can give some time can find a volunteer job in paleontology.

Dr. David R. Yesner
Department of Anthropology
University of Alaska
3211 Providence Drive
Anchorage, Alaska 99508
907-786-1630

Ages: 18 and up

Qualifications: No special skills required.

Costs: $600 for a six-week program includes food, daily transportation, and equipment. You provide personal gear and tents.

The University of Alaska is excavating the Broken Mammoth Site, an ancient campsite nearly 11,800 years old. Although this is an archaeological rather than a paleontological project, it includes the recovery and analysis of large mammal and bird bones from the late Ice Age. Participants are taught techniques in surveying and excavating such sites.

Crew surveying for fossils in Glendive, Montana. Photo by Ethan Hill, Milwaukee Public Museum, Milwaukee, Wisconsin.

Volunteer Coordinator
Royal Tyrrell Museum of Palaeontology
Box 7500
Drumheller, Alberta, Canada T0J 0Y0
403-823-7707

Ages: 18 and up.

Qualifications: Interest, good physical condition.

You provide personal gear; the museum provides room and board.

At the Royal Tyrrell Museum, which has discovered major fossils in Alberta, volunteers play a key role. The Summer Field Volunteer Program has been in operation at the Royal Tyrrell since the early 1980s. Volunteers stay for a minimum of three weeks and spend their time at various field camps throughout Alberta, where they experience hands-on training in all aspects of paleontology. A small number of volunteers are accepted to work in preparation and research labs, the library, and public areas of the museum. The field program begins in June and continues to the end of August.

Denver Museum of Natural History
2001 Colorado Boulevard
Denver, Colorado 80205-5798
303-370-6387

Not only does the Denver Museum use volunteers as docents, leaders of fossil workshops, helpers for kids' camp-ins in the dinosaur halls, and in the preparation of fossils, but they also offer a Certification Program in Paleontology that provides in-depth background in paleontology for amateur paleontologists and educators. The intensive one-year curriculum includes training in fieldwork, fossil preparation, collection management, general paleontology, and research methods. Other special opportunities are periodic undergraduate and graduate student assistantships. Summer field schools are available which provide on-site experience for amateur and student paleontologists.

Carefully removing a fossil, surrounding rock and all. Courtesy American Museum of Natural History, New York.

(Pages 108-109) *Apatosaurus* and family once frequented the area now known as Dinosaur National Monument in Utah.

. John Horner, Curator of Paleontology
useum of the Rockies
ntana State University
zeman, Montana 59715
ll Dig-a-Dinosaur at 406-994-3170

es volunteers regularly for site work in Montana. In
)2 they surveyed the Hell Creek Badlands in
)koshika State Park, Glendive, Montana, for a
ndup of Montana's earliest livestock — *T. rex* and
ceratops. Overnight programs in paleontology at
g Mountain in the summer are available for families
h kids 10 and older. Two-week-long programs for
ticipants 12 and older allow you to assist at the digs
l the Paleo Field School. A fee of $900 for a two-
ek session covers room, board, and training.

ordinator of Volunteers
veland Museum of Natural History
de Oval, University Circle
veland, Ohio 44106
-231-4600

: Cleveland Museum of Natural History uses volun-
's to catalog and prepare specimens and for outreach
grams.

v Mexico Museum of Natural History
unteer Programs
l Mountain Road, N.W., P.O. Box 7010
uquerque, New Mexico 87194-7010
-841-8837

New Mexico Museum of Natural History employs
unteers as docents and also behind the scenes in the
aration and cataloging of fossils and preparation
repair of exhibits.

Volunteers and staff from the Milwaukee Public Museum
ing at Glendive, Montana. Photo by Ethan Hill.

Milwaukee Public Museum
800 West Wells Street
Milwaukee, Wisconsin 53233
Attn: Dr. Peter M. Sheehan, Curator of Geology

Dr. Sheehan routinely works in Montana and uses
volunteers in his activities.

Volunteer Program
National Museum of Natural History
10th Street and Constitution Avenue, N.W.
Washington, D.C. 20560
202-357-1300

The Smithsonians's active program uses volunteers
from junior high age on up. Several noted museum
scientists got their start here.

Volunteers may work as docents in museums. Courtesy Utah
Museum of Natural History, Salt Lake City.

8
Dinosources:
Books, Catalogs, & Other Stuff About Dinosaurs

Almost everything you can think of from pencils to pajamas has been embellished with dinosaurs. If you know a dinomaniac, you might want to write for some of the following.

Books & Tapes for Young People

Aliki. *Digging Up Dinosaurs.* New York: Thomas Y. Crowell, 1981. 32 pages. Color illustrations by the author. A terrifically popular introduction to dinosaur discovery by one of the best and most-loved children's science writers.

Aliki. *Dinosaurs Are Different.* New York: Thomas Y. Crowell, 1985. 32 pages. Color illustrations by the author. Ages 5–9. In her own creative way, Aliki explains how dinosaurs are classified according to special characteristics such as skull and hip structure.

Bates, Robin, and Cheryl Simon. *The Dinosaurs and the Dark Star.* New York: Macmillan, 1985. 48 pages. Illustrated. Ages 8–12. Up-to-date discussion of new extinction theories including comets and "Killer Star."

Branley, Franklyn M. *Dinosaurs, Asteroids, and Super-stars.* New York: Thomas Y. Crowell, 1982. 84 pages. Illustrated. Ages 9–13. Volcanoes, supernovas, asteroids, and climate changes: why did dinosaurs become extinct?

Cobb, Vicki. *The Monsters Who Died.* New York: Coward-McCann, 1983. 64 pages. Illustrated. A good description of how paleontology works. Paleontologist detectives unlock ancient mysteries through fossil clues.

Craig, Annabel. *The Usborne Book of Prehistoric Facts.* London: Usborne Publishing, 1986. 48 pages. A colorful cartoon history of prehistoric life from the Big Bang to writing. Fun, loaded with facts.

Elting, Mary, and Ann Goodman. *Dinosaur Mysteries.* New York: Platt and Munk, 1980. 61 pages. Illustrated. Well-researched, highly recommended presentation of recent dinosaur research.

Elting, Mary. *The Macmillan Book of Dinosaurs and Other Prehistoric Creatures.* New York: Macmillan, 1984. 80 pages. Illustrated. A good overview of dinosaurs.

Haplocanthosaurus delfsi towers over visitors to the Cleveland Museum of Natural History in Ohio.

(Right) Open wide! *T. rex* at the Academy of Natural Sciences of Philadelphia. Photo by David Bennett.

Freedman, Russell. *Dinosaurs and Their Young*. New York: Holiday House, 1983. 32 pages. Illustrated. Ages 6–9. The discovery of dinosaur babies and nests with theories on how dinosaur families lived.

Halstead, Beverly. *Brontosaurus, The Thunder Lizard*. New York: Golden Books, 1982. Illustrated. 32 pages. Ages 7–12. Basic brontosaur biology with a close look at one individual.

Halstead, Beverly. *Deinonychus, The Terrible Claw*. New York: Golden Books, 1983. 32 pages. Illustrated. Ages 7–12. Every event presented in the life of a young female *Deinonychus* is based on fossil evidence.

Horner, Jack, and James Gorman. *Maia: A Dinosaur Grows Up*. Running Press, Philadelphia: 1985. 36 pages. Illustrated. Follow the life of a baby duckbill written by the paleontologist that discovered her nest. Terrific illustrations. Write the Museum of the Rockies, Montana State University, Bozeman, MT 59717; $4.95.

Jacobs, Francine. *Supersaurus*. New York: G.P. Putnam and Sons, 1982. 48 pages. Illustrated. Ages 5–10. Highlights of paleontologist "Dinosaur" Jim Jensen's discovery of a giant sauropod.

Lambert, David. *A Field Guide to Dinosaurs*. New York: Avon Books, 1983. Illustrated. Index. 256 pages. Ages 10 and up. A generously illustrated guide to dinosaurs throughout the world, arranged by orders, with information on evolution, extinction, paleontology, and museum collections.

Rydell, Wendy. *Discovering Fossils*. Mahwah, New Jersey: Troll Associates, 1984. 32 pages. Illustrated. Well-written and illustrated introduction to fossils.

Sattler, Helen. *Baby Dinosaurs*. New York: Lothrop, Lee & Shepherd, 1984. 32 pages. Illustrated. Fossil discoveries provide excellent speculations on the life of baby dinosaurs from one of the best writers for a young audience.

Stein, Sara. *The Evolution Book*. New York: Workman Publishing, 1986. 389 pages. Illustrated. Index. Ages 10–14. One of the best explanations of evolution – adults will learn something too – by a creative, well-informed science writer for children. Fascinating to dip into.

Valerie, Michele, and Michael Stein. *Dinosaur Rock*. New York: Caedmon, 1984. TC 1739. Audiotape. A rock and roll audiotape introduction to dinosaurs that will get your kids' toes tapping and teach them about dinosaurs.

Wexo, John. *Prehistoric Zoobooks*. San Diego: Wildlife Education, 1990. Illustrated. A boxed set of 10 booklets covering life on earth with family activities, posters and a time chart. Highly recommended. Write to Wildlife Education, 930 West Washington Street, San Diego, California 92103. $29.95.

Diplodocus — 140 million years old and 70 feet long, discovered in Johnson County, Wyoming, in 1902 — now resides at the Houston Museum of Natural Science in Texas. Photo by J. Griffis Smith.

...ks For Adults

...isks (*) indicate books consulted in writing ...osaur Digs.

...Bakker, Robert T. *The Dinosaur Heresies: New Theories Unlocking the Mystery of the Dinosaurs and Their Extinction.* New York: William Morrow, 1986. Illustrated. Index. An exciting look at the cutting edge of dinosaur theory by one of the leading proponents of the new theories.

* Colbert, Edwin H. *The Great Dinosaur Hunters and Their Discoveries.* New York: Dover Publications, 1968. Illustrated. Index. The story of dinosaur paleontology with all the earliest surmises, feuds, and amazing discoveries.

* Fenton, Carroll Lane, and Mildred Adams Fenton. *The Fossil Book.* Garden City, New York: Doubleday and Company, 1958. Illustrated. Index. A good basic explanation of fossils from the earliest find to the Pleistocene.

* Horner, John R., and James Gorman. *Digging Dinosaurs: The Search That Unraveled the Mystery of Baby Dinosaurs.* New York: Workman Publishing, 1988. Illustrated. Join Horner day by dusty day over six years as he stripped away rock and dirt to go back 80 million years and discovered one of the most significant fossils of this century: *Maiasaura,* the good mother lizard.

* Kurten, Björn. *Before the Indians.* New York: Columbia University Press, 1988. Beautifully illustrated. Index. An interesting, highly readable account of the Pleistocene: tar pits, ice ages, mammoths, and mastodons.

* Lambert, David. *A Field Guide to Dinosaurs.* New York: Avon Books, 1983. Illustrated. Index. An extensive catalog of dinosaurs and their families.

* Lessem, Don. *Kings of Creation: How a New Breed of Scientists is Revolutionizing our Understanding of Dinosaurs.* New York: Simon and Schuster, 1992. Illustrated with excellent drawings and photographs, many by the author. Index. A brand new look at modern paleontologists by the founder of The Dinosaur Society, who has accompanied many of them in their field research.

* Paul, Gregory S. *Predatory Dinosaurs of the World: A Complete Illustrated Guide.* New York: Simon and Schuster, 1988. Illustrated. Index. An up-to-date look at the fascinating predators of the Mesozoic Era.

* Wilford, John Noble. *The Riddle of the Dinosaur.* New York: Random House, 1985. Illustrated. Index. An excellent overview of dinosaur controversies from the early teeth discovered by the Mantells in the last century to modern theories about warm-bloodedness and intelligence.

Dinosources

• One of the best places to order books as well as slides, videos, and posters is The Dinosaur Nature Association, P.O. Box 127, Jensen, Utah 84035 (or call 1-800-845-DINO). DNA operates bookstores in both Dinosaur National Monument and Dinosaur Quarry. A $5 annual membership fee entitles you to a 20% discount. Proceeds go to the National Park Service.

• For T-shirts, models, pencils, posters, cassettes, jewelry, stamp pads and more, write for The Dinosaur Catalog, a 24-page catalog that improves every year: P.O. Box 546, Tallman, New York 10982; or call 914-634-7579.

• For a more serious, adult collector, SAURUS is an 8-page listing of T-shirts and popular books, plus opportunities to buy rare books on dinosaurs from the 1800s and early 1900s. Write SAURUS, 530 South 4th East, Centerville, Utah 84014.

• The Dinosaur Society. For the paleontologist in your family, a membership in the Dinosaur Society might be just the ticket. This nonprofit corporation supports dinosaur research, publishes several newsletters to keep members up to date, and offers other membership benefits including family field trips to dig sites in North America and overseas. Write The Dinosaur Society, P.O. Box 2098, New Bedford, Massachusetts 02741; or call 508-997-2467.

Younger paleontologists might enjoy joining the Dinosaur Club and receiving their monthly newsletter *DINO TIMES* for $19.95. Write P.O. Box 87069, South Dartmouth, Massachusetts 02748; or call 508-990-8809.